MEASURING THE INVISIBLE WORLD

ANTONI VAN LEEUWENHOEK,
LID VAN DE KONINGHLYKE SOCIETEIT IN LONDON.
Geboren tot Delft, A. 1632.

A mezzotint of Leeuwenhoek by Verkolje made in 1686

A. Schierbeek *Ph D*
Editor-in-Chief of the Collected Letters of A. v. Leeuwenhoek
Formerly Lecturer in the History of Biology in the University of Leyden

MEASURING THE INVISIBLE WORLD

The Life and Works of Antoni van Leeuwenhoek F R S

With a biographical chapter by
MARIA ROOSEBOOM *Ph D*
Director of the National Museum of the History of Science at Leyden

ABELARD-SCHUMAN
London and New York

ABELARD-SCHUMAN LTD.
London and New York

PREFACE

Half a century ago as a young boy at school I first became acquainted with the works of Leeuwenhoek. Some ten years later I bought a copy of his letters published in Dutch and gradually Leeuwenhoek became a friend, as he has become to many other research workers in the field of microscopy. In 1931 the Leeuwenhoek committee of the Royal Dutch Academy of Sciences was formed and in 1942 I became editor-in-chief of the Collected Letters of A. van Leeuwenhoek. My original interest had now developed into a serious study.

The Leeuwenhoek committee rightly decided to keep to the chronological order of the letters written over a period of fifty years. In most letters Leeuwenhoek discusses a number of subjects and these subjects are often dealt with again in later letters. This of course does not simplify the study of the letters and their subject matter.

My opinion is that it is only possible to form a sound judgment of Leeuwenhoek and his research into various problems by a systematic study and collection of material on each subject. The development of Leeuwenhoek's thought and his methods of solving a problem can thus be more clearly understood. His conclusions are sometimes difficult to understand and experts are often called in to repeat his experiments, frequently with surprising results. Even the original language construction is hard to follow and needs further expert attention. Nevertheless his letters make fascinating reading, though they are bound to lose something in translation despite the best efforts of translators. The translations used are those dating from Leeuwenhoek's period with the assistance of my sister-in-law, Mrs. D.

Oterdoom-Tiemersma, and of Professor R. J. Forbes, to both of whom I am indebted. Dr. Maria Rooseboom, director of the National Museum of the History of Science at Leyden, has made some important contributions, including the biographical chapter. The object of this book is to further interest in Leeuwenhoek and simplify the problems involved in reading his work. I consider it a privilege that this edition should appear in the *Life of Science* series which is headed by a book from that great man of the history of science, Dr. George Sarton. The Collected Letters naturally remain the foundation for any deeper study of Leeuwenhoek's research, and it would be desirable to await the completion of this great work. This task, however, will not be completed before another half century and in my opinion our present generation has much to learn from the study of Leeuwenhoek. That is why I have been pleased to comply with the request of the publishers and write this book which I hope will increase interest in, and make new friends for, this great scientist.

For various reasons the publication of this book has been delayed but this has provided me with the opportunity to insert further material and to obtain the assistance of Dr. and Mrs. Savile Bradbury of Oxford with the problems of the English translation.

A. SCHIERBEEK
The Hague, 20 Jan 1959

ACKNOWLEDGMENTS

Author's and Publishers' thanks are due to Dr. and Mrs. Savile Bradbury of Oxford University for their help in preparing the manuscript for press.

CONTENTS

ILLUSTRATIONS

CHAPTER ONE

Leeuwenhoek's Life in the Republic of the United Netherlands

MARIA ROOSEBOOM

Delft

The visitor who, nowadays, happens to take a walk through the snug, tidy centre of the old city of Delft will find there many features that have remained unchanged since the time when Leeuwenhoek lived and worked in the town, over two centuries ago. The district which today is a maze of narrow canals and streets was, in those days, the centre of one of the most important cities of Holland, surpassed only by Amsterdam and Leyden in matters of industry, business, shipping and general importance. For a long time now its prominence has been exceeded by Rotterdam and other towns, but even today, on crossing the Great Market of Delft, one is impressed by the stately spaciousness of the stone-paved square, and at the end of it the tower of the New Church pointing its spire heavenward, still just the same as when Leeuwenhoek could see it from his desk.

To those with a knowledge of architectural style, however, this monument of religious architecture is not such an eloquent witness to the greatness of Delft in the first half of the seventeenth century as the Town Hall opposite, where Leeuwenhoek spent so many hours of his life. This Town Hall may appear rather small to us nowadays, but its architect, 13

Hendrik de Keyzer, who designed it after the great fire of 1618, gave it a finer, grander and more international air than most similar secular buildings possessed at that time. It is built entirely in natural stone, and its design reminds one of the old Italian and French styles of architecture.

Delft owed its prosperity and importance to its numerous industries and to its position as a seaport. The town's most famous products were beer, textiles and, from about 1600 onwards, chinaware; sea-going vessels could sail right up to Delft via Delftshaven, to fetch their cargoes of tiles and pottery for export, and the East India Company also had an office and warehouse in the city. By the end of the sixteenth century, however, Delft had already begun to decline from its peak of prosperity and importance; most of the breweries closed down, and Rotterdam, profiting by its geographically more favourable position, began to outstrip Delft.

It was in this centre of bustle and industry that, on October 24th, 1632, Antoni van Leeuwenhoek was born, the fifth child of Philip Thonisz. and Grietje Jacobsdr. van den Berch. Philip was a basket-maker by trade, as his own father had been before him, at the Oosteinde (East End), on the corner of a small street called Leeuwenpoort, and there is little doubt that the family name is derived from the position of the house.[1]

The basket-maker's trade may seem rather a modest occupation, but the packing of the famous Delft-ware must have required an enormous number of baskets, and it seems likely that the father had a fairly large business: certainly the house at Oosteinde was no humble dwelling, and its façade was large enough to accommodate five windows in its width. It also seems probable that Antoni's mother came from a better-class family, for her grandfather and several of her great-uncles were merchants of considerable importance. Her father was the only one of a large family who became a

14

brewer, and since this was at a time when the brewing industry was on the decline, we may suppose that, after his death in 1615, his seven children did not live in ease and abundance. It seems therefore as if Leeuwenhoek's mother belonged to the least prosperous branch of a family which was generally highly respected, and from which had come many City Fathers.

The Dutch Republic

The City Corporations held an important position at this time in the decentralized governmental system of the Republic of the United Netherlands. They were formed from the most powerful among the burgesses, for after the western provinces had liberated themselves from Spanish domination in about 1580 the burgesses were able to take control because there was neither a strong royal family, nor a conservative feudal nobility, nor any ecclesiastical power with sufficient strength to seize the reins of government and establish a firm central authority.

Thus, in the Republic, the bourgeoisie had become the ruling class and they radiated energy and enterprise, supplementing the work of the guilds (which continued to confine themselves to their traditional fields of activity) and exploiting the possibilities of new branches of industry, commerce and finance. Anyone who was willing to work and take risks could climb the social ladder and make his mark in life; indeed, work was highly respected in the Republic. Karel van Mander wrote in his 'Schilder-boek' (Painters' Book) in 1604, 'In my opinion, a better custom prevails among us Netherlanders than among other peoples, namely that parents, however rich they may be, have their children taught some craft, art, or trade while they are still young.'

The self-assured 'Regents' (as the City Fathers were called) set an example; they were industrious and sober-minded, thrifty and free from corruption, always striving to surround

15

themselves with an atmosphere of simplicity and solid re-
spectability. With only very rare lapses into speculative
schemes (such as the great gamble in tulip-bulbs!) the
Regents lived in their fine houses along the canal banks,
and were filled with a sense of reality; despite their
Protestant uprightness, they had a perfectly liberal, open-
minded, business-like attitude to life. These qualities
made the influence of the middle-class felt all over the
world.

The geographical position of the Republic was favourable
both for sea-going trade and colonization, and at first foreign
competition was not very keen. Antwerp, which was still
under Spanish domination, saw its prominence as a world
market taken from it by Amsterdam; at this time England
still lagged behind the Republic in economic development.
The Dutch East India Company, founded in 1602, rapidly
outrivalled its counterparts, which existed simultaneously
in England, France, Denmark and Sweden.

It is not surprising that the cultural life of the Republic,
too, bears the stamp of the prevailing economic and civic
mood. This is plainly evident in the Dutch school of painting
at that time and in the contemporary architecture, sculpture,
and music, none of which shows any 'aristocratic' influences.
The contribution of Leeuwenhoek's native city to these arts
is sufficiently well-known: painters like Pieter de Hoogh, Jan
Vermeer, Carel Fabritius, Emanuel de Witte, Willem van
Helst, and Willem van Mierevelt have, indeed, attained im-
mortality. Delftware articles, both useful and ornamental,
are admired in museums all the world over.

Leeuwenhoek's youth

Only the first few years of Leeuwenhoek's youth were
spent in Delft. When he was five he lost his father, and he
left home three years later, in the same year as his mother
married again. Her second husband, Jacob Molijn, was a

16

'City Painter and Bailiff of the Common Finances.' Antoni Leeuwenhoek received his early education at Warmond and later at Benthuizen—two small towns between ten and twenty miles from Delft. According to Boitet, who wrote a history of Delft, Antoni lived in Benthuizen with an uncle on his mother's side who was the local sheriff and bailiff; he had another uncle in the same town who was a notary and city clerk.

It is probable that it was here that Antoni acquired the foundations of the mathematical and administrative knowledge which were to prove so useful to him in later life. He never learned any foreign languages or Latin, which were not necessary for someone engaged in either the law or commerce: with Dutch one could make oneself understood in any foreign port in those days. It seems, moreover, that his teachers had no great cultural aspirations for young Antoni, for even in the use of his mother tongue he gives evidence of only slight literary powers. He himself says, in one of his first letters, that he has 'neither style nor pen.' Nevertheless, in the course of the fifty years during which we can follow his use of the language we can observe distinct development and improvement and with his terse, straightforward prose he generally manages to state his views very clearly and in considerable detail.

His early training did not provide that manual dexterity which his extremely refined work eventually demanded of him. From several of his letters it is clear that by his own efforts he gradually acquired the necessary skill in metal working and glass grinding. He was endowed with a high degree of both commonsense and patience, and these qualities, together with his extraordinary powers of observation and his sharpness of vision, formed the basis of his unique achievements.

In 1648, when he was about sixteen years old, there was a change in Antoni's life: in that year, so Boitet tells us, he

B

moved to Amsterdam where he was employed by a draper as book-keeper and cashier—surely a remarkable position of trust for such a young man. In all his hundreds of letters, Leeuwenhoek himself does not give us any description of his youth or of his life in Amsterdam; we know nothing whatever of his experiences at that time, of his way of life, or of his emotions when, in later life, his thoughts went back to those years.

Boitet tells us that Leeuwenhoek, in spite of his responsible post, ' . . . managed, by dint of extraordinary industry, to find enough time to learn the cloth-worker's trade and to pass the master's test in six weeks'—a somewhat surprising statement, since the Amsterdam cloth worker's guild usually demanded a training period of three years. Although it is not known how many employers Leeuwenhoek had while in Amsterdam, it recently became known that in 1653 he was in the service of a Scottish merchant by the name of William Davidson, who, since the previous year, had been established in a new district of Amsterdam called ' 't Nieuwe Eylant.' Van Seters has published a document which is a deed of proxy authorizing Leeuwenhoek to act on Davidson's behalf in business transactions. The reason for this full authorization is probably to be found in the first naval trade-war between Holland and England, which was then in progress and which may have made it difficult for the Scot to do any business in Holland; perhaps Leeuwenhoek merely acted as a figure-head for him.

Settlement at Delft

It was probably in 1654 that Leeuwenhoek left Amsterdam. We do not know whether his prospects there were unfavourable, or whether he, who later gave such ample proof of an independent mind, was anxious to stand on his own feet, or even whether it was his future wife, Barbara de Mey, who lured him back to Delft. All we know is that Leeuwenhoek, after his return to Delft and his marriage on July 29th, 1654, carried on a trade in cloth and haberdashery; two receipts dated 1658 and 1660, respectively concerning the sale of silk, cloth, kersey, bombazine, buttons, ribbon, etc., are still in existence. The fact that Leeuwenhoek was in trade in Delft is also suggested by the conditions of mortgage payment on the house which he purchased for five thousand guilders. The interest on the mortgage (of four thousand guilders) could be paid either in money or in goods. The house was named 'The Golden Head' and was on the Hippolytusbuurt canal.

Barbara de Mey, who was the daughter of a serge draper, was not to live long at Leeuwenhoek's side. She died in 1666, leaving him with the only one of their five children to survive childhood, his ever-faithful daughter and companion, Maria, who never married and who never ceased to attend to her father's needs until his death many years later. In 1671 Leeuwenhoek married his second wife, Cornelia Swalmius, who was to share his life until her death in 1695 made him for the second time a widower. It is possible that meanwhile he had given up his haberdashery business and was chiefly engaged in his civic duties, having inherited some money from his mother's family.

Leeuwenhoek's official functions

In 1660 Leeuwenhoek was appointed 'Camerbewaarder der Camer van Heeren Schepenen van Delft' (Chamberlain of the Chamber of the Worshipful Sheriffs of Delft) and in 1669, after passing the required examination, he was admitted to the profession of surveyor. In 1676 he was appointed trustee of the insolvent estate of the deceased painter Jan Vermeer, and in 1679 he was made a wine-gauger to the city of Delft—all of these being posts which required an able and trustworthy man. In addition to these, from 1677 onwards he was 'Wijkmeester-generaal' (General District Supervisor).   19

The income attached to these functions was far from large; his basic salary must have been about five hundred guilders a year, in addition to which there were his fees for wine-gauging and he may have earned something as a surveyor, but this is not certain. It is unlikely that his total income from all these duties could have exceeded eight hundred guilders a year. His capital must have amounted to about sixteen thousand guilders in 1674, since his assessment in a capital levy that year, the 'hundredth penny' tax, was one hundred and sixty guilders. At an interest rate of three per cent (which later he sometimes charged other people, including his relations) this capital should have yielded about five hundred guilders a year. In later years his capital increased considerably, partly by legacies but also, without doubt, by careful and business-like management. When his daughter Maria died in 1745, the father's and daughter's estates together were worth over 90,000 guilders, and there is certainly no doubt that Leeuwenhoek lived in comfort. Apart from the house which he occupied, he had another house in Delft, which he had inherited from his second wife's family; in 1666 he already had one or two gardens outside the town and a cottage with apple and cherry trees, while in 1681 it appeared that he also owned a horse.

It is very difficult to get a clear idea of the actual demands on Leeuwenhoek's time made by his various appointments, whether they kept him busy and whether he had to do all the work himself. He occasionally complained that pressure of work left him so little time for microscopy, and we know that the regulations laid down for the wine-gauger demanded that he should do at least part of the work himself. It was his task to check the volume of the wine and oil barrels, and the regulations demanded that the gauging of all barrels filled for the first time in Delft should be done by him personally. The duties of Chamberlain are less clearly defined although he is enjoined 'to keep to himself whatever he may overhear in the Chamber.' On the other hand it is strange to think that the very next passage in the regulations could have been intended for a well-to-do man like Leeuwenhoek himself: ' . . . to clean the aforesaid Chamber properly and to keep it neat and tidy; to lay the fire, when the season requires such, in due time, and carefully to preserve to his own profit what coals may remain unconsumed.' It seems that the post of 'Wijkmeester-generaal' was hardly more than a sinecure.

If our impression is correct, we may say that Leeuwenhoek, without ever rising to a high official post, was a highly esteemed citizen of Delft, who doubtless owed his position, first and foremost, to his personality. His integrity and ability made him eminently fitted for positions of trust, but it is also quite possible that his influential relatives were in part responsible for his various appointments.

The custom of offering certain posts which carried small incomes and required very little work to persons related to members of the City Corporation began to come into vogue in Holland during the second half of the seventeenth century. By about the middle of the century the Regents no longer had possibilities of unlimited expansion, for in a series of naval wars the Republic was forced to defend its overseas trading interests against an increasingly powerful England, while on the Continent forces had always to be available to resist Louis XIV's aspirations to inflict on Europe his 'general monarchy.' The Regents, in order to secure for themselves a continuing and increasing prosperity, cut themselves off from the lower classes more and more. One of their ways of achieving this was to develop an aristocratic form of social intercourse (adopting French as the 'society language') and to follow the cultural and artistic lead of France. At the same time the Regents lost some of their sturdy energy: enterprising merchants became smug, sedate magistrates, and the businessman who had feathered his nest built himself a fine country house and henceforth lived on the interest

21

from his investments. This was not a time of great and stirring events, but one of stabilization and consolidation. Wealth and position in preceding generations were kept carefully within a certain limited circle, for the City Fathers had learned how to divide among themselves the privileges which were dependent upon their own influence and authority. It is not impossible therefore that Leeuwenhoek, who, especially through his mother, was related to the City Corporation, owed some of his appointments to this kinship, and that he had arranged for most of the actual work required of him to be done by others.

In the post of Chamberlain to the Worshipful Sheriffs of Delft he succeeded his cousin by marriage, Jan Strick, whose wife, like Antoni himself, was a grandchild of the brewer Jacob Sebastiaansz. van den Berch. The influence of this prominent Delft family may therefore be suspected, although there is no evidence on this point to be found in the archives. In 1699, when he was sixty-six years old, Leeuwenhoek was given an official assistant, while retaining his full salary, and five years later he was also given an assistant for his wine-gauger's post. Perhaps this was merely the official recognition of a situation that had already existed for a long time, namely that the holder of such posts would arrange for some other man to do the actual work for him—though again we have nothing definite to show that this is what happened in Leeuwenhoek's case.

Leeuwenhoek himself, who speaks with complete candour about all sorts of domestic details, tells us nothing at all about his official activities; however, one thing is certain—that the attitude of gentlemen of independent means was always alien to his personality. True, in his letters we observe development of greater linguistic ability and greater self-assurance but he does not adopt any refined artificial airs. He learns no foreign languages, and never, even in front of the most eminent visitors, does he attempt to

22

conceal his status as a simple citizen who, entirely by virtue of his own ability and energy, made his name in the world. There are passages to be found in his letters which clearly have some connection with his methods of work as a surveyor and wine-gauger. This is especially true in connection with his evident desire and ability to apply measurement and calculation in order to get an estimate of the size and number of his microscopic objects (cf. p. 48). Although we cannot escape the fact that Leeuwenhoek alone among the classical microscopists[2] successfully applied the quantitative method to microscopy, it would be wrong to attribute this solely to his practical experience as a surveyor and wine-gauger; measurement was one of the most characteristic features of that exact natural science which began to develop with such impetus during the seventeenth century.

The beginning of Leeuwenhoek's work with the microscope

It is not known with any certainty when Leeuwenhoek began to move in scientific circles. One thing, however, is certain—that there was no-one with any academic training among his uncles or great-uncles, and his first wife was also one of a family of tradesmen and industrialists. Upon his second marriage, to Cornelia Swalmius in 1671, two years before his first letter was submitted to the Royal Society, a relationship with persons who had received a university education became evident for the first time. Cornelia's father was a clergyman and her brother a physician; she herself may have known Latin, for she signed herself Swalmia rather than Swalmius on a deed drawn up by a notary. It is, however, fairly certain that she was unable to translate either Latin or English books for her husband. One would thus be tempted to suppose that Leeuwenhoek's keen interest in nature was stimulated by Cornelia's father and brother, although it is equally possible that his love of learning dated from much earlier, when he was living in Amsterdam. Boitet

23

states that shortly after his first marriage (in about 1655) Leeuwenhoek started, without any previous training, to study navigation, astronomy, mathematics, 'philosophy' (that is to say natural science and physics), and 'physics' (what we would now call biology). The first demonstrable fruit of these studies might well have been his appointment fourteen years later as a surveyor in 1669, just before his second marriage.

At first Leeuwenhoek also wrote about physical problems; for instance he wrote to Robert Boyle about the barometer experiment, and he was interested in the question of dissolving air in water. To Christiaan Huygens he gave a model of the axial movement of the earth and the atmosphere, and he also invented an anemometer. However, he lacked the necessary training in physics to be able to contribute substantially to this field of study, and his later observations on such subjects are accordingly few and far between. We know that Huygens presented him with a copy of his *Astroscopia*, written in 1684, of his *Traité de la Lumière* and *Discourses de la Cause de la Pesanteur*, written in 1690; these must have been more or less courtesy presents though, for Leeuwenhoek never mastered the French language.

Leeuwenhoek must have been familiar with the use of the magnifying glass since he was in the cloth trade, where it was commonly used for inspecting the quality of the tissue and the weaving. Of course, it is possible to observe considerable detail with a simple lens of this kind, but a magnifying glass alone could never have enabled him to make the spectacular discoveries which he later achieved. As a matter of fact, he tells us in one of his first letters (1673) that he had succeeded in devising and constructing efficient microscopes only a short time before.

The period of guesswork concerning Leeuwenhoek's activities ends when the Delft physician Reinier de Graaf introduced him to the Royal Society in a letter dated April 28th,

24

1673 (in the middle of the third Dutch-English naval war!).
In the *Philosophical Transactions* of the Society (VIII, no.
94, p. 6,037) de Graaf's recommendation is made as
follows:

' . . . that one Mr Leeuwenhoek hath lately contrived
Microscopes excelling those that have hitherto been made by
Eustachio Divini and others; adding, that he hath given a
specimen of their excellency by divers Observations, and is
ready to receive tasks for more, if the Curious shall please
to send him such. . . .'

As a matter of fact, the Society's secretary, Oldenburg,
sent Leeuwenhoek a request to that effect, and with this a
contact was established which was to be maintained with
varying intensity for nearly fifty years, ending only with
Leeuwenhoek's death.

The 'New Philosophy'

It was no mere accident that it should be the Royal Society
which enabled Leeuwenhoek to publish his investigations.
The Society, a body of scientists young both in years and
spirit, was indeed the centre for the study of the new science;
it was buzzing with eager activity and sought to correspond
with members all over Europe.

In the seventeenth century we observe a definite intellectual expansion, springing from the static, authoritative
mediaeval way of thinking. Knowledge of nature and of
remote countries and their inhabitants had rapidly increased,
while many technological inventions had expanded the possibilities open to industry and greatly enriched human existence. The skilled craftsmen in whose hands these new
inventions were further improved gradually won for themselves an increasingly important place in economic and
cultural life, and the new intellectual acquisitions soon
played too prominent a part in general thinking for mediaeval
conceptions to remain completely satisfying. Architects,

mining engineers, cloth makers, dyers, chemists, surgeons, gold- and silversmiths, instrument makers, surveyors, cartographers, navigators and even merchants lived in a continual state of concern with the realities of this world. After all, they owed their prosperity to these realities, and they were in the habit of using them as the practical test of their ideas. As a rising class, moreover, they were more inclined to regard society as a dynamic process than as a hierarchical edifice existing under static conditions. It was inescapable that scientific thinking should also feel the influence of, and respond to, this situation.

The 'New Philosophy' holds that nature can only be known and understood when the laws by which it is ruled are known. The method to be pursued in the study of nature is exemplified by astronomy, which since time immemorial has owed its exact development very largely to the needs of navigation. In fact, astronomy was the first science which used measurement to collect its factual data, from which it drew general conclusions by comparison and calculation. It is this method which during the seventeenth century revolutionized science. Careful measurement had shown that not only the mechanism of the heavenly bodies but also such earthly phenomena as the path of an object when dropped or thrown, hydrostatics, the refraction of light and so forth, could be expressed by quantitative laws.

The 'New Philosophy' soon achieved such successes that its adherents were filled with great optimism about the benefits which they would be able to confer on humanity, ' . . . for the process of Art is indefinite, and who can set a *non-ultra* to her endeavours?' (Power, 1661). There was no doubt a close connection between the optimistic attitude towards life of the bourgeoisie, and the general confidence in natural science, based upon the scientist's own observations and personal ability. Boyle regarded the study of nature as

26   ' . . . a work to the glory of God and the benefit of Man,'

and Baxter asserted that ' . . . knowledge is to be valued according to its usefulness.'

The 'philosopher' addressed himself not only to the 're-public of scientists' but also to the burgesses who were un-prejudiced by scholastic education, and yet perfectly com-petent to form a reasoned opinion; as Descartes says ' . . . le bon sens est la chose du monde la mieux partagée' (good judgement is one of the more evenly distributed attributes in the world). An increasingly large number of publications on the new science came to be written in the authors' native languages and were read by a wide public.

Parallel with this development there occurred a change in the attitude of philosophy and religion towards natural science. As a result of the new faith in rational thought accep-ted from Descartes, the admiration of God as revealed in nature assumed an intellectual rather than an emotional or aesthetic form: the complexity and order prevailing in nature were now adduced as proofs of His wisdom and omnipo-tence. Cartesian doctrines created unity of religious faith and knowledge: reason has been given to us so that we can learn to know God from His works, for why should we study only God's word, not the work of His hands? Science, said Francis Bacon, ' . . . is the handmaid of religion'; Jan Swammerdam praised the study of the anatomy of the bee ' . . . because God's wisdom is so mathematically proven therein.'

Descartes recommended mathematics to the world as being the purest form of reason, and the increasing application of mathematics to the problems of natural science led to a brilliant development of mathematical technique. Stevin had introduced decimal fractions; Napier and Bürgi had invented logarithms; Pascal constructed the first calculating machine; Descartes, by introducing the analytical method, made it possible to solve geometrical problems mathematically and to represent movements by linear diagrams; and finally

27

Newton and Leibnitz found in differential calculus a method for the mathematical computation of curves.

With the development of mathematical methods for the treatment of collected data, a need began to be felt for additional aids in obtaining the data themselves. A number of different instruments for observation and measurement were invented in quick succession. The telescope was used in astronomy for the first time by Galileo in 1609; the compound microscope appeared about 1620 and shortly afterwards the strongly magnifying simple lens (weak lenses had been known for a long time, but were hardly ever used for scientific purposes). In 1612 the thermometer was invented and in 1643 the barometer; the pendulum clock was developed in 1656, while various instruments for specific experiments such as the air pump (about 1640) and the 'electrical machine' (1660) made their appearance.

Attempts were also made to introduce measurement to biology. Santorio, a pupil of Galileo, determined the frequency of the pulse by using a pendulum, took the temperature of a feverish patient with a primitive thermometer, and measured his weight in relation to his own metabolism. Descartes almost completely separated the mind from the body in his philosophy, and thereby prepared the way for an explanation of all the vital phenomena with the aid of mechanics, that most successful of all the new branches of science. The living organism was represented as a machine and muscular action, perception and conveyance of stimuli, metabolism, growth and the like, were approached from a mechanistic point of view. Harvey made observations concerning the valves of the veins and on the estimated capacity of the heart and the frequency of the pulse, which led him to the conclusion that the views of Galen (Galenus, a Greek physician born in A.D. 130) on the ebb and flow of the blood were incorrect. When, in 1628, Harvey announced his conclusion that there is a continuous flow or circulation of the blood he

28

gave considerable encouragement to the new mechanistic school of thought.

The Royal Society

It was inevitable that all these enlightened modern thinkers should seek contact with one another, especially because they had to meet some formidable criticism, and they were fewer in number than we sometimes realize today, accustomed as we are to lay stress on their great achievements when we speak of the seventeenth century.[3] However, they were re-inforced and encouraged by the keen patronage of many people who were not themselves academically trained lovers of learning. Mutual exchange of views and experiences furthered the formation of groups, often quite unconnected with university life. The names of the first Italian Acade-mies, for instance, are very significant; in 1603 there was founded the 'Accademia dei Lincei' (Academy of the Lynx-eyed) and in 1657 the 'Accademia del Cimento' (Academy of the Experiment).

In England, too, there already existed the nucleus of a similar group before the Cromwellian revolution. Boyle, in 1646, mentions 'our new philosophical college, that values no knowledge but has a tendency to use.' After the Restoration this learned company came out into the open and from about 1660 meetings were held in Gresham College, London, while in 1662 the group received its Royal Charter as the 'Royal Society of London for the Improving of Natural Knowledge.' It was this young group which, supported by Royal patron-age, became the core of the international organization of the new science. Its members were given the task of recruiting as many important correspondents abroad as possible, and the Society asked of these correspondents, ' . . . no extra-ordinary preparations of Learning; to have sound Senses and Truth is with them a sufficient Qualification' (Sprat). Thus it came about that the unlettered burgess of Delft,

Leeuwenhoek, was introduced in 1673 into this company by his medical townsman Reinier de Graaf, who had already been welcomed as a correspondent on the grounds of his work in anatomy.

Leeuwenhoek's scientific career

Leeuwenhoek's first letter was received with a certain benevolent, sympathetic reserve, but the Society asked for further drawings and observations, which no doubt filled our amateur with grateful satisfaction. His second letter, written some months later, testifies to his modesty, and to the difficulties with which he had to cope, alone as he was in this branch of scientific research.

Meanwhile, the statesman Constantijn Huygens the elder, one of the most learned Dutchmen of his time and a great promoter of the arts and sciences in Holland, had written to Oldenburg, Secretary of the Royal Society, giving him information on Leeuwenhoek's personality and character: '... he is a person unlearned both in sciences and languages, but of his own nature exceedingly industrious and curious ... I trust that you will not be unpleased with the confirmations of so diligent a searcher as this man is, though always modestly submitting his experiences and conceits about them to the censure and correction of the learned.' This very accurately sketches the main features of Leeuwenhoek's personality as we know it from his 280 or so letters: a patient and persevering investigator of nature, gifted with an extraordinarily keen vision and powers of observation; modest and accessible to the opinions of others, but conscious of his own worth, and thoroughly honest. As the guiding thought in his work, one may take the aphorism found in Leeuwenhoek's handwriting above a picture of him by Jan Goeree, 'Door Arbeijt en Naarstigheijt komt men tot Saaken, die men te vooren onnaspeurlijk agten' (By diligent labour one discovereth matters that before one hath deemed inscrutable).

30

To this we must add his deep religious assurance, his complete faith in the 'All-wise Creator,' a never-flagging admiration for the perfection of the most minute, hidden mysteries of the work of His hands and the conviction that his researches would surely help to make His Omnipotence more universally known. Without ever lapsing into high-flown phrases he repeatedly gave evidence of his religious faith: 'Let us lay the hand on our mouth, and reflect that the All-wise hath deemed this needful for the reproduction of all that hath received movement and growth, and so, the why and the wherefore we can but guess after' (July 10th, 1696).

On many occasions Leeuwenhoek had to fight for his ideas, and, while he was generally successful in the argument, in some cases he was obliged to recant an opinion he had previously expressed, which he invariably did in the most frank and generous terms. As an example we may take his theory that all matter was built up from tiny 'globules.' This notion failed to find ready acceptance in scientific circles, and Christiaan Huygens, the renowned scientist, who for many years maintained a friendly and cordial relationship with Leeuwenhoek, accordingly wrote to Oldenburg on January 30th, 1675, 'Je voudrais bien scavoir quelle foy on adjoute chez vous aux observations de nostre Monsieur Leeuwenhoek qui convertit tout chose en petites boules. Pour moy apres avoir en vain tasché de voir certain choses qu'il voit, je doute fort, si ce ne sont pas des déceptions de sa vue . . .' (I should like to know what faith you attach to the observations of our Monsieur Leeuwenhoek, who has converted all things into small globules. After having, in vain, sought to see certain things which he sees, I very much doubt if these be not weaknesses in his eyesight.)

At first Leeuwenhoek refused to modify his ideas: 'Thou sayest, sir, that there are persons of great good judgement, at Paris and elsewhere, that do not admit the globule that I

31

have discovered in a variety of bodies; I am in no way troubled by this, what I have wrote in that regard is veritably true, and if it so might be that the learned persons lived in our Holland, I would invite the same to come and see the globule in most of the parts that I have spoken of.' A few years later, however (May 31st, 1678), writing about dentine, he asserted straightforwardly that ' . . . we were led into error.' Dentine, the substance which constitutes much of the teeth, apparently consists of 'tubules.'

Christiaan Huygens was not long in recognizing the simple, unlettered investigator as an authority on microscopy. After he had observed for himself the movement of the flagellae of uni-cellular organisms, he wrote on November 18th, 1678, to his brother, 'Je voudrais bien scavoir ce que Leeuwenhoek diroit de tout ceci' (I would like to know what Leeuwenhoek would say about this), and again, some weeks later, 'Sachons ce qu'en dira Leeuwenhoek.' ' Let us know what Leeuwenhoek would say of this.'

Dodart, Louis XIV's personal physician, was so impressed by Leeuwenhoek's work that, as early as 1677, he wrote to Christiaan Huygens: 'Il me semble que des gens de ce mérite devroient avoir pension comme Académiciens externes. N'aura-t-on pas tous ses mémoires en françois ou en latin en un petit volume?' (It seems to me that people of this worth should have an allowance as external Academicians. Would you not like to have all his writings in one volume of either French or Latin?) Dodart's appeal, however, met with little response. The Académie des Sciences did not bother much with microscopy, and Leeuwenhoek's name is mentioned only once, in passing, as a correspondent of one of the members.

Meanwhile our indefatigable microscopist continued his observations, carefully writing down any of his discoveries which he considered important. Only rarely did he deal with
32   a single subject as a complete entity; again and again he

reverted to subjects dealt with in previous letters, until he felt that they had been fully and adequately discussed. As a result his letters often seem desultory to us, but Leeuwenhoek's investigations were far from unsystematic. For year after year he continued unswervingly the study of certain subjects, such as reproduction, steadily reporting his new findings as they arose.

The discovery of micro-organisms

A great sensation was caused in the scientific world by his discovery of micro-organisms, not, as a matter of fact, on his very first mention of their existence in the water of Lake Berkel (September, 1674) but two years later, when, in a letter dated October 9th, 1676, he described a great number of details concerning animalcules which he found in his water-butt, in well-water and sea-water, and in a pepper infusion. He described numerous Protozoa on the basis of his daily notes, and it is evident from his measurements that he was the first to observe bacteria. At the Royal Society, this famous letter at first met with considerable scepticism. Members were at first unable to see Leeuwenhoek's 'little animals' in pepper-water, so Hooke and later also Grew set to work to repeat the observations. From April until November 1677 their results remained negative, but on November 15th Hooke was able to give the Royal Society a successful demonstration of the animalcules. The discovery of the existence of these tiny creatures was eventually brought to the attention of King Charles II, who thereupon bade the Royal Society give him a demonstration. After this Leeuwenhoek's name was on the lips of everyone, in high society, as well as in the scientific world. Thus, in five years he had won a name for himself by his work, and only the jealous and malevolent (for example Hartsoeker) dared to cast doubt upon his observations or dispute the importance of his discoveries. The esteem and prestige which Leeuwen-

33

c

hoek had acquired in the world of science was based very largely on the reliability of his observations, and on the unfailing sureness with which he differentiates between observation and speculation. He ranks the former, as an aid to knowledge and understanding, far above the latter.

Elected Fellow of the Royal Society

It was a great surprise and joy to Leeuwenhoek when, in 1680, he was unanimously offered a Fellowship of the Royal Society, surely the highest honour one could then receive in the scientific world. Leeuwenhoek was obviously moved by this mark of esteem and on receiving the certificate,[4] which had been worded for his benefit in the Dutch language, he wrote to Robert Hooke (who was then the Secretary of the Society and who probably had given very considerable encouragement to the appointment), that he ' . . . contemplated the document with great affection and my heart filled with gratitude; and with respect to you, Sir, I am bounden to say that not only this day but all the days of my life, I am and will remain, Sir, with great thankfulness, your most obliged, Antoni Leeuwenhoek.'

This feeling of gratitude never left him, for when in 1717 he felt his strength diminishing he wrote, 'Methinks these will be the last observations I shall be able to send you honourable Gentlemen, because my hands grow weak and suffer from a little shakiness, which is due to my far advanced years, a good eighty-five having passed me by. And so I send you with this my deep thankfulness, because in the year 1679 you were so kind as to elect me, quite beyond my competence, a Fellow of the most worthy College of the Royal Society. . . . For all these honours and gifts aforesaid, I herewith convey to you my gratitude once more.'[5]

Certainly Leeuwenhoek's contact with the Royal Society was of very great value to him. On being elected a Fellow he had become a famous man, and the publication of his letters in the *Philosophical Transactions* made his work known all over the world, while any suggestions or criticism from London stimulated him to make further investigations. As a result of this contact he developed from an isolated amateur into an honoured research worker with world-wide associations.

Visitors

Learned and eminent visitors flocked to Delft in order to see his discoveries, and as early as 1680 Constantijn Huygens the Younger wrote to his brother Christiaan, 'Tout le monde court encore chez Leeuwenhoek comme le grand homme du siècle' (The whole world still comes to pay homage to Leeuwenhoek as the great man of the century). Crowned heads and princes came to see him, including King James II of England, Czar Peter of Russia, King Frederick I of Prussia, Landgrave Carl of Hessen, and the Elector of Saxony, Augustus II. Queen Mary of England, arriving unexpectedly, found the Delft burgess away from home, a fact which, so he wrote, ' . . . will, and must, be mourned by me all my life.' Out of gratitude for the honour done to him by the Queen, he dedicated to her the publication of the Third Continuation of his Letters (1692).

Leeuwenhoek must have undoubtedly learned as much from his scientific visitors as they from him. He certainly had lengthy discussions with them, learning many things which, owing to his ignorance of languages, he was unable to glean from books. Unfortunately, Leeuwenhoek himself often omitted to mention names when quoting the opinion of visitors or other authors, so that we are not aware of all the contacts that he actually made. With regard to works in the Dutch language there is frequent evidence that Leeuwenhoek read some of the authors such as Stevin, and for his surveyor's examination he must have studied books on

35

geodesy. He was also acquainted, probably through contact with other people, with the experiments of Santorio on metabolism, with Descartes' ideas, the observations of Malpighi on the development of the hen's egg, and with Hooke's *Micrographia*, while the corpuscular theory of matter linked him with Boyle.

Although Leeuwenhoek's lack of learning was undeniably a barrier to the establishment of scientific contacts, it had the advantage that he was completely free from any scholastic prejudices. In the way in which he tackled his problems, he exhibited a freshness, a practical approach and a common-sense which are satisfying to the reader and, more important, very often led him to the correct conclusions. His theoretical speculations give evidence of a simple, mechanistic method of reasoning. He mentions Descartes in very respectful tones, although he does venture to disagree with him on the possible form of the component particles of water. It is possible that Leeuwenhoek derived his mechanistic ideas very largely from Theodorus Craanen who had been the first to lecture in Leyden University on Cartesian medicine in 1670, and who repeatedly visited Leeuwenhoek in the course of the next decade. Others who must have undoubtedly discussed Cartesian ideas with him were Constantijn and Christiaan Huygens, both of whom, as we have seen, maintained a cordial relationship with him. Several of Leeuwenhoek's letters were also addressed to the Cartesian physician of Utrecht, Lambert van Velthuysen; and Jan Swammerdam, the micro-anatomist, often visited him even before 1675.

It was certainly an impressive array of scientific associates that Leeuwenhoek had collected for himself so early in his career. To those mentioned above must be added the visitors from abroad, first and foremost the delegates from the Royal Society who (since Leeuwenhoek never came to England or attended a session of the Society) came over to find out what their remarkable fellow-member was like, and to study his

work on the spot. We know for certain that Thomas Molyneux, David Gregory, and Hans Sloane visited Leeuwenhoek,
and doubtless many others did so. The Englishmen must
surely have brought a good interpreter with them, for during
the first few years of his Fellowship Leeuwenhoek complained that he knew no one in Delft who could make a
proper translation of the Royal Society's letters. As Antoni's
fame grew, the number of his visitors increased to an almost
alarming extent, and he was obliged to become selective with
regard to those he received. He stated in 1711 that in the
space of four days he had had to receive twenty-six callers,
every one able to produce an introductory letter (with the
exception of a duke and an earl!). Thus, in order to have
some time left for himself he had to send many people away.

Those who were admitted to the sanctuary must have been
shown many different kinds of research material. There
would usually have been some small live fish for the demonstration of the capillary circulation, collections of gall insects
or larvae of fleas, plant-lice, and his sealed glass tubes containing oyster embryos. Here, too, they might find jars of
crystallizing salts, while infusions of pepper, cloves and nutmeg would be side by side with samples of rain-water and
ditch-water. Finally, carefully put away in tin boxes, there
were his numerous small microscopes, some of which he had
made specially for studying a particular specimen, together
with his razor with which he could cut the thinnest of plant
sections.

Leeuwenhoek had a certain number of demonstrations
which he showed to visitors—the corpuscles of the blood and
the capillary circulation, the ciliary movement on the gill of
the mussel, the embryos of oysters, sections of human skin,
the eye of a fly, etc. These were observations which did not
require very great magnification; in fact he kept his best
microscopes to himself, a form of professional secrecy which
was quite common in those days. Only reluctantly did he

37

give away any of his technical secrets, for instance when it was unavoidable in order to dispel the doubts of a correspondent about the reliability of his observations. Being financially independent, Leeuwenhoek never sold any of his microscopes, neither was he at all generous in giving them away. So far as we know, he offered one or more to Queen Mary of England, possibly also to Czar Peter the Great and to Constantijn Huygens the Elder; anyone else who wished to see them had to go to Delft. Leeuwenhoek never had any pupils to whom he taught the art of grinding lenses, for he had very little confidence in the earnest attempts of the younger generation for this extremely refined and delicate work, and to accept pupils ' . . . would reduce me to a state of slavery.'

Scientific supporters and opponents

Leeuwenhoek's most persistent and morally quite unworthy opponent was the sordidly ambitious Hartsoeker, who disputed among other things the priority of his discovery of spermatozoa. Leeuwenhoek was not in the least intimidated by him, and in 1715 he wrote to his London colleagues: 'It hath come to my knowledge that Hartsoeker enjoyeth little esteem among the learned, and when I saw in his writings that he presumed to state untruths, and hath great self-conceit, I have looked into his writings no further.' The Italian physician and biologist Vallisneri could not agree with his animalcule theory, but this did not worry Leeuwenhoek very much either, for he said in the same letter 'We have in our country a proverb that "one woodcock does not make a winter"; if Vallisneri be against my statements, there are a thousand for me.' For had not the great Boerhaave, in his *Sermo Academicus de Comparando certo in Physicis*, testified to his belief in the truth of the animalcule theory, and did not Leibnitz also take a favourable attitude towards his investigations? Where, then, was the necessity for him to trouble any further with the opinions of inferior scientists?

Great indeed was the homage paid to Leeuwenhoek by the Louvain college of Professors, 'The Wild Boar.' In 1716 this learned company had a silver medal struck in his honour on which, in addition to his portrait, there was a bee-hive with the legend 'In tenui labor attenuis non gloria.' The laudatory poem which accompanied the medal moved the already aged researcher to tears, and once again induced him to give expression to his innate dignified modesty: ' . . . for I know myself so far, that I am not for the hundredth part worthy of the expressions that you have made concerning my poor labours, for they spring only from an inclination that I have to inquire into the origins of the things created, in so far as it is possible for me.'

Publications

Leeuwenhoek had been in retirement from his official posts for some time, so he was able to give all his time to microscopy. Most but not all of his hundreds of letters were addressed to the Royal Society, and sometimes one letter to London would immediately be followed by a second of almost the same content dispatched to another correspondent. Doubtless this was a safety measure to ensure that his observations should be recorded in duplicate, for a letter might easily be lost on the way to London. Moreover, the Secretaries of the Royal Society were not at all prompt either in acknowledging receipt of the letters or in publishing them in the *Philosophical Transactions*. This delay in acknowledgment caused Leeuwenhoek considerable distress, for, although he always liked to give everyone his due, he disliked being denied the credit for discoveries which were rightly his. About 1694 there is evidence that he was getting somewhat tired of these delays and there comes a period when he turned to other 'Personages of High Standing and Learned Men,' which was not unusual in his day. His correspondents formed a gallery of notable figures: the Elector Palatine, the Landgrave of

39

Hesse-Cassel, Magliabecchi (librarian to Cosimo III of Tuscany), the Burgomasters of Delft, Amsterdam and Rotterdam, the Board of the Dutch East India Company, Antonie Heinsius (Grand Pensionary), later Commissary of The Republic to England, Frederik Adriaan, Baron of Rheede van Renswoude, Leibnitz, Tschirnhaus, were among the most important.

Our simple research worker never thought of writing a book, and indeed even the writing of his letters must have been quite difficult for him at first. In fact, it was only reluctantly that he let himself be persuaded by de Graaf to make a written record of his first observations. Most of his letters have been published in different combinations and translations either verbatim or in extracts. The first publication in Holland of some of his letters was made without his knowledge, but for the publication of later volumes he personally placed his letters at the disposal of certain publishers. His later letters to various correspondents frequently contain an offer of one or more of these volumes.

His last years

Leeuwenhoek evidently enjoyed excellent health and his remedy for minor ailments consisted of drinking great quantities of tea to thin down the blood! About 1707, however, he complained of pain in his legs and of shakiness in his hands, and he told Boerhaave in 1716 that he thought his 'entrails are worn out.' Not long afterwards he was troubled with shortness of breath, and in November 1717 he wrote a touching farewell letter to the Royal Society, believing it to be his 'swan-song.' His iron constitution rallied, though, and both his mind and his vision remained clear. He sent eighteen more letters to the worthy company in London, the last one being dictated on his death-bed, while a lung disorder which lasted only six days was draining away his last remaining strength. The end came on August 26th, 1723, two months before his ninetieth birthday. The church bells tolled thrice as, five days later, the mortal remains were carried with great ceremony to the Old Church nearby.

As a last greeting from Leeuwenhoek, Newton received on November 7th, on behalf of the Royal Society, 'A Cabinet containing Twenty Six Microscopes left to them by the Late Mr Antoni van Leeuwenhoek.' This legacy was accompanied by a letter from his daughter Maria, then sixty-seven years old, a letter breathing the same simple dignity as had been her father's. With great piety Maria guarded her father's heritage. The poisonous remark made by Uffenbach, to the effect that Leeuwenhoek refrained from selling any of his microscopes so that his daughter might later be able to ask a higher price for them, was not in any way justified, for not until 1747, two years after Maria's death, were they sold, which was eventually done by public auction, when the gold specimens were disposed of by weight.

Leeuwenhoek's life appears to have been calm and un-ruffled. His travels were few; he visited the chalk cliffs of England about 1668 in the period before we know anything of his microscopical activities and in 1698 he was in Antwerp, where he visited the Jesuit Van Papenbroek. Apart from these travels, we hear only of holiday trips in Holland and visits to relations.

Though his life was uneventful, it was certainly not with-out grief; he lost his father when he was only five and his mother when he was eleven. His first wife died twelve years after their wedding and of their five children only the faithful Maria survived infancy. His second wife died in 1695, after twenty-three years of married life, and, as far as we know, the only child of this union died whilst still a baby.

Antoni's kinsfolk were a varied group of people and we know from his two last wills and testaments (1719 and 1721) that he did not maintain an equally friendly relationship with them all, though his letters never refer to any family troubles. 41

Anyone who wishes to learn more about Antoni van Leeuwenhoek should read his letters, which two and a half centuries later give us a far more personal contact with the author than can be achieved by reading a mere biography. He who delves into this fascinating literature will surely feel that he has found a new friend.

CHAPTER TWO

Leeuwenhoek and
His Microscopes

History

It is sometimes stated that Leeuwenhoek invented the microscope, but this is not strictly accurate. Seneca mentions the use of small hollow glass spheres, filled with water, for magnifying purposes, and the Arabs were well acquainted with the functions of lenses. In the West, Roger Bacon, who, as early as the thirteenth century, studied lenses with particular care, proposed the use of spectacles and predicted the invention of the microscope. As a matter of fact, the identity of the inventor of the microscope is not known with any certainty. It is frequently claimed that Zacharias Jansen made the first microscope in 1590 at Middelburg, but De Waard has shown that Jansen was born in 1588, and his son, who is supposed to have helped him, in 1611. Galileo, working in Italy, seems to have made a microscope about 1610, and one of the members of the Accademia dei Lincei, Stelluti, published in 1625 the first drawings made with the aid of a microscope. The first book wholly devoted to microscopy was the famous *Micrographia* written by Hooke in 1665; his microscope was a compound instrument, with a very small plano-convex object glass and a large plano-convex lens as an eye-piece. Grew, Malpighi, and Swammerdam soon followed with their microscopical studies, at the same time as Divini was constructing microscopes in Italy.

43

Leeuwenhoek's first letter

On May 7th, 1673, the members of the newly established Royal Society of London first heard of Leeuwenhoek through a letter, written during the midst of the Dutch war, from the famous Reinier de Graaf:

'That it may be the more evident to you that humanities and science are not yet banished from among us by the clash of arms, I am writing to tell you that a certain most ingenious person here, named Leeuwenhoek, has devised microscopes which far surpass those which we have hitherto seen, manufactured by Eustachio Divini and others. The enclosed letter from him, wherein he describes certain things which he has observed more accurately than previous authors, will afford you a sample of his work: and if it please you and you would test the skill of this most diligent man and give him encouragement, then pray send him a letter containing your suggestions, and proposing to him more difficult problems of the same kind.'

This first letter (the original of which is missing) was published in the *Philosophical Transactions* in May 1673, together with an introduction by the Secretary of the Royal Society, Mr Oldenburg. In this he says 'that one Mr Leeuwenhoek' has made the observations, and 'doubtless will proceed in making more observations, the better to evince the goodness of his glasses.' This was, as Dobell remarks, 'a prophecy which was actually fulfilled more amply during the next fifty years than anybody could then have thought possible.'

Contained in this first letter were observations on the structure and growth of mould; on the mouthparts, sting and eye of the bee; and on the mouthparts, feelers and legs of a louse.

Leeuwenhoek saw in the 'knobs at the ends of the stalks of the mould, some blossom-like leaves,' an observation

44

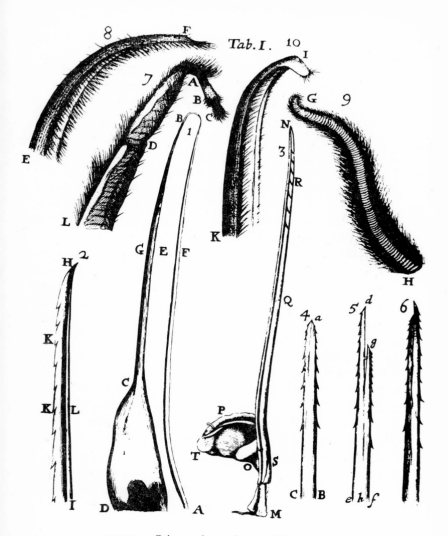

PLATE I *Sting and mouthparts of bee (reduced)*

which led the famous microbiologist Kluyver to remark that there was every reason to conclude that Leeuwenhoek had actually seen the spores of moulds; Hooke had seen the sporangia before this, but not the contained 'seeds.'

'The sting of a bee I find to be of another make than it has been described by others,' wrote Leeuwenhoek, referring to the faulty opinion of Hooke, who was not, however, mentioned by name in this letter. Leeuwenhoek later realized that his own description of the structure of the sting was inaccurate, for he corrects his account in a subsequent letter. The parts of the mouth are well described by him; it is interesting to note, however, that the mobile lobe of the tongue—the so-called 'spoon'—had already been noticed by Swammerdam in 1670, though his description was not published until 1737.

Leeuwenhoek saw the facets of the bee's eye, and found that the 'horns' of the louse had 'five joints . . . others marked but four.' Here again Leeuwenhoek is referring to Hooke, though it is possible that Hooke studied an intermediate stage between the larva, which has three joints in each antenna, and the adult louse which has five. In this first letter, Leeuwenhoek said that the 'sting of the louse was at least five-and-twenty times less than one single hair,' a remark which led the Dutch poet Hoogvliet to say in an early edition of Leeuwenhoek's letters: 'Here the dimensions of the invisible are determined with fixed measures.' It is a remarkable fact that Leeuwenhoek in his letter corrects Hooke, one of the most able scientists of the age, no less than three times! These first observations have illustrations and these, together with the detailed descriptions, enable us to conclude that the magnification was about thirty to forty diameters (Plate 1).

These results make one wonder what was the construction of Leeuwenhoek's microscopes, and how he used them to obtain his knowledge.

The construction of Leeuwenhoek's microscopes

All simple glass lenses have two chief faults, known technically as spherical and chromatic aberration. When seen through such a lens, straight lines at the margin of the field of view appear curved, and the edges of objects appear fringed with blue and yellow. When two or more of these simple lenses are used in a microscope, these flaws will be intensified; it was probably because of this that Leeuwenhoek did not use a compound microscope with two or more lenses, but worked with simple 'magnifying glasses.'

Martin Folkes, who examined the instruments bequeathed to the Royal Society in 1723, described them as follows:

'For the construction of these instruments, it is the same in them all, and the *Apparatus* is very simple and convenient. They are all single Microscopes, consisting of a very small double-convex glass, let into a socket, between two silver plates riveted together and pierced with a small hole. The object is placed on a silver point, or needle, which, by means of screws of the same metal, provided for that purpose, may be turned about, raised or depressed, and brought nearer or farther from the glass, as the eye of the observer, the nature of the object, and the convenient examination of its several parts may require.' (See Plate 2.)

'Mr Leeuwenhoek fixed his objects, if they were solid, to this silver point, with glew; and when they were fluid, or of such a nature as not to be commodiously viewed unless spread on glass, he first fitted them on a little plate of talc, or excessively thin-blown glass, which he afterwards glewed to the needle, in the same manner as his other objects. . . . The glasses are all exceedingly clear, and shew the object very bright and distinct, which must be owing to the great care this Gentleman took in the choice of his glass, his exactness in giving it the true figure; and afterwards, amongst many, reserving such only for his use, as he, upon trial,

47

found to be the most excellent. Their powers of magnifying are different, as different sorts of object may require; and, as on the one hand, being all ground glasses, none of them are so small, and consequently magnify to so great a degree as some of those drops, frequently used in other microscopes; yet, on the other, the distinctness of these very much exceeds what I have met with in glasses of that sort.'

Magnifying and resolving power

Some years later, in 1740, Baker determined the focal lengths and the magnifying powers of the Royal Society's microscopes. These latter results, however, were expressed for an image distance of eight inches, so that, as the commonly accepted standard is now ten inches, Dobell remarks (quite rightly) that all Baker's magnifying powers represent only four-fifths of their values as expressed in modern notation; for example, the 'largest magnifier' did not magnify 160 but 200 diameters.[6] The magnifying power, however, is not the most important property of a microscope; more important is the clarity of the image, which is largely dependent on the 'resolving power' of the microscope. The resolving power is a measure of the ability of the instrument to distinguish small objects as separate, although they are very close together, and the 'resolution' is often expressed as the smallest distance by which two points can be separated, for them still to appear distinct from one another. Two microscopes may have the same magnifying power, but the one with the greater resolving power will give the clearer image. Modern microscopes may have an almost unlimited power of magnification, but their resolution is limited to about 0.25 μ. As the Royal Society's microscopes are unfortunately lost, their resolving powers cannot be measured.

During his lifetime Leeuwenhoek made about 550 microscopes, of which only the following are known to be still in existence.

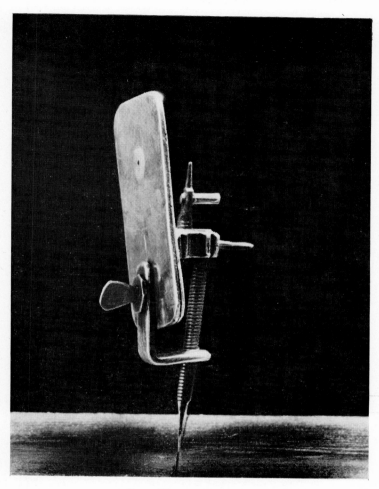

PLATE 2 *One of Leeuwenhoek's microscopes*

3 made of silver (now in Leyden, Munich and Jena)

6 made of brass (two in Leyden, one in Utrecht, one in the possession of Miss Haaxman, one in Antwerp, and one in Paris)

1 'aalkijker' with 5 lenses (an instrument for viewing the blood circulation in the tail of an eel). Possibly made by Leeuwenhoek and now in Leyden.

Miss Rooseboom has studied both the microscopes in the museum at Leyden and the specimen in the possession of Miss Haaxman; the microscope in Utrecht has been examined by Van Cittert; and that at Antwerp by Frison.[7] The best specimen, that at Utrecht, has been shown to have a magnifying power of 270 times and a resolving power of 1.4μ.*

It is interesting to speculate whether the lens of the Utrecht microscope, with its 270 diameter magnification, was the best that Leeuwenhoek ever made. In this connection, Dobell remarks: 'The known magnifying power of his best glasses was, of course, sufficient to enlarge objects as small as blood-corpuscles (and even bacteria) to visually perceptible dimensions, a fact which modern workers with the compound microscope seem to overlook.' Again, Folkes writes:

'But however excellent these glasses may be judged, Mr Leeuwenhoek's discoveries are not entirely to be imputed to *their* goodness only: His own great judgement and experience in the manner of using them, together with the continual application he gave to that business, and the indefatigable industry with which he contemplated often and long the same subject, viewing it under many and different circumstances, cannot but have enabled him to form better judgements of the nature of his objects . . . than it can be imagined any other person can do, that neither has the experience, nor has taken the pains this curious Author has so long done. . . .

* $1\mu = \dfrac{1}{1,000}$ mm.

D

'I have rather insisted on this, as it may be a caution to us, that we do not rashly condemn any of this Gentleman's observations, tho' even with his own glasses, we should not immediately be able to verify them ourselves.'

Other relevant observations on this subject are found in Dobell, who writes: 'Leeuwenhoek had unbounded patience and magnificent eyesight—as his works abundantly testify—but he could not perform miracles'; and in the writings of Thomas Molyneux who visited Leeuwenhoek by order of the Royal Society in 1685. Molyneux says 'but besides these (microscopes) he told me he had another sort, which no man living ever looked through setting aside himself; these he reserves wholly for his own private observations.' While it seems certain that Leeuwenhoek had very good microscopes for private use, we still have no knowledge of the performance of his best lenses; his letter of November 12th, 1680, gives us, I think, a hint which may throw some light on this problem.

'For my own part, I can say with truth, that the smallest sort of which I shall here speak, I see alive and exhibit as plainly to my eye as one sees, with the naked eye, little flies or gnats sporting in the air, though they may be more than a hundred million times less than a coarse grain of sand' (diameter about 870μ), ' . . . indeed, in one sort I see the very hairs on their mouth' (=the cilia?).

'As they will say it is not credible that so great a many of these little animalcules can be comprehended in the compass of a sand-grain . . . and that I can make no calculations of this matter, I have figured out their proportions thus, in order to exhibit them more clearly to the eye: Let me suppose, that I see a sand-grain but as big as the spherical body ABGC (Plate 3) and that I see, besides, a little animal as big as D, swimming or running on the sand-grain; and measuring it by my eye, I judge the axis of the little animal

D to be the twelfth part of the axis of the supposed sand-grain AG; consequently, according to ordinary rules, the volume of the sphere ABGC is 1,728 times greater than the volume D. Now I suppose I see, among the rest, a second sort of little animals, which I likewise measure by my eye through a good glass giving a sharp image, and I judge its axis to be the fifth part (though here I allow it to be but the fourth part) of the axis of the first animalcule D; and so, consequently, the volume of fig. D is 64 times greater than the volume of fig. E. This last number, multiplied by the first

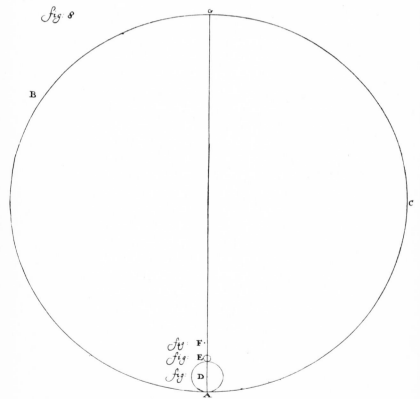

PLATE 3 *Leeuwenhoek's comparison of sizes of objects (reduced)*

number (1,728), comes then to 110,592, the number of the little animals like E which are as big as the sphere ABGC. But now I perceive a third sort of little animalcules, like the point F, whereof I judge the axis to be only a tenth part of that of the supposed animalcule E; wherefore 1,000 animalcules such as F are as big as one animalcule like E. This number, multiplied by the one foregoing (110,592), then makes more than 110 million little animals like F as big as a sand-grain.

'Otherwise I reckon in this fashion: Suppose the axis of fig. F is 1, and that of fig. E is 10; then, since the axis of fig. D is four times as great as that of fig. E, the axis of D is forty. But the axis of the big sphere ABGC is twelve times that of fig. D; therefore the axis of AG is equal to 480. This number multiplied by itself, and the product again multiplied by the same number, in order to get the volume of ABGC, gives us the result, as before, that more than 110 million living animals are as big as a grain of sand.'

Now the diameter of F in the figure is exactly that of a sand-grain, and Leeuwenhoek says 'suppose I see a sand-grain but as big as the spherical body ABGC'; in other words, 'I see the sand-grain at least as great as ABGC,' so that if we assume the figure is to scale, then the magnification would be the ratio of the diameters of F and ABGC, which is about 480 times. From this it would appear that Leeuwenhoek had lenses with a magnifying power of about 500 diameters.

Dark-ground illumination

Leeuwenhoek also said 'with my particular method of observing . . .', but does not tell us what his method was. Dobell, however, was almost certain 'though I cannot prove from his own words that I am right. I am convinced that Leeuwenhoek had, in the course of his experiments, hit upon some simple method of *dark-ground illumination*. He was, as we

52

know, well aware of the ordinary properties of lenses; and he tells us himself that he used concave magnifying mirrors and employed artificial sources of illumination (e.g. a candle). Consequently, he may well have discovered by accident—or even purposely devised—some method which gave him a clear dark-ground image. . . . In a very early letter (January 22nd, 1675) he writes " . . . but I can demonstrate to myself the globules in the blood as sharp and clean as one can distinguish with one's eyes, without any help of glasses, *sandgrains that one might bestrew upon a piece of black taffety silk.*" . . . It is idle to speculate on *how* he may have achieved this result.'

Swammerdam wrote in his famous *Biblia Naturae* that Leeuwenhoek showed him the sporangia of a mould 'with a microscope in accordance with the invention of Hudde, Mayor of Amsterdam,' who made his microscopes with blown glasses and with a condenser lens. Harting quotes Bonanus (1691) as mentioning 'de Monconny's visit to de Hud (=Hudde), Mayor of Amsterdam, who showed him a microscope with a simple lens and a second lens throwing light on the object'; from this, it seems certain that de Hudde used a condenser. This is in accord with the view of Van Seters, who thinks that Leeuwenhoek used a small concave mirror and also a condenser lens.

When the Uffenbachs visited Leeuwenhoek, on December 4th, 1710, they 'further inquired of Mr Leeuwenhoek whether he ground all his lenses, and did not blow any? He denied this, and displayed great contempt for the blown glasses. . . . He said they were all ground in the same grinding cup. . . .' It follows from this, I think, that the invention of Hudde, used by Leeuwenhoek, was not his blown lenses, which were in common use, but may have been the condenser lens. With this instrument, and with oblique illumination, it would be easy to obtain a dark-field illumination and thus see the objects brightly lit against a dark background.

Modern experiments

In 1941, T. Y. Kingma Boltjes published a paper entitled 'Some experiments with blown glasses' in which he describes photomicrographs with a magnification of 460 and 575 times which were taken through a lens with a diameter of 0·60 mm. He adds 'It is much easier to make observations with a simple lens than one could expect at first view. . . . My experiments led me to the conclusion, that even if van Leeuwenhoek had known the dark-ground illumination, it would have been of little use to him as the one-sided illumination causes distortion. . . . My second conclusion is, that van Leeuwenhoek must not necessarily have had better microscopes than the one in the charge of the museum of Utrecht (resolving power $= 1·4\mu$).' Kingma Boltjes also tried to explain the words of Leeuwenhoek (October 9th, 1676): 'My method for seeing the very smallest animalcules . . . I do not impart to others, nor yet that for seeing many animalcules at once, but I keep that for myself alone.' In the meniscus (the curved surface of water in tubes) Van Cittert pointed out that micro-organisms can be observed rather easily; Kingma Boltjes thinks that Leeuwenhoek may have realised this, and may also have used coverslips, but he concludes: 'In all probability the actual methods of van Leeuwenhoek will never be known to us.'

I. Barnett Cohen (1937) wrote that he could easily obtain a dark-ground effect by the lateral illumination of a capillary tube with a small globe at its lower end. This was especially the case if one or more air bubbles were introduced into the liquid filling the globe. He also showed that Leeuwenhoek's little lenses could very well have been used for water-immersion. For this purpose he simply put a drop of water on the lens of a horizontal microscope. As a consequence of the slow evaporation of the drop, there would be a time when the surface was exactly at the focus of the lens, so that any minute bodies on this surface could be seen very distinctly for a short time. Sarton remarks: 'Each instrument or method is, as it were, a crystallization of human genius,' words which are very appropriate to Leeuwenhoek as both instrument and method were his own inventions!

Micrometry

Leeuwenhoek was not the first microscopist, but he was the first to *measure* microscopic objects. He had to select objects which could serve as standards of comparison, one of the first of which was an inch. He has given a good figure of a five-inch measuring rod, which shows that he was very accurate, as this works out at an average value of 2·61 cm. to the inch.

A coarse sand-grain, he says, has a diameter of approximately 1/30th of an inch which is equivalent to about 870μ (July 25th, 1684).

A fine sand-grain Leeuwenhoek estimated at 1/80th or 1/100th of an inch, which gives an average value of 260μ (May 20th, 1679, March 3rd, 1682), whilst in his letter of May 31st, 1678, he says '2½ times the diameter of a hair from my beard equals a fine sand-grain,' so that its diameter must be about 100μ; a hair from his head proved to be about 60–80μ in diameter.

'*A hair from my wig*' was used by him in order to estimate how many hairsbreadths go into one inch (letter of May 20th, 1679). Leeuwenhoek put a hair from his wig on one of the thirtieth subdivisions of an inch on his brass rule, and he thought that twenty hairs would go into 1/30th of an inch, which works out at 600 hairsbreadths being equivalent to an inch and therefore, in modern notation, one hair would have a diameter of about 43μ. This suggests that his wig was made of the hair of the Angora goat, the hairs of which have a length of up to 35 cm., and a diameter of 40–43μ; it is known that the hair of this animal was used throughout the Netherlands in Leeuwenhoek's time for wig-making.

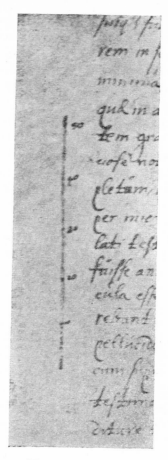

PLATE 4 *The counter of Leeuwenhoek*

The eye of a louse proved to measure 50–85μ, whilst its hairs varied from 2–9μ.

The red blood cell was measured by Leeuwenhoek. In his letter of June 1st, 1674, he remarks: 'I judge the red globules of the blood to be quite 25,000 times smaller than a fine sand-grain.' Leeuwenhoek gives its volume so that we may

56

compute the diameter of a red blood corpuscle to be 8.5μ. In his letter of June 25th, 1684, he says 'the complete globules that make our blood red are so small that a hundred of them laid length-wise would not make up the axis of a coarse sand-grain or 1/3,000th of an inch.' We now know that the diameter of a human red blood corpuscle is about 7.2μ.

Animalcules in pepper-water. Leeuwenhoek wrote on December 26th, 1678, that '30,000,000 of these animalcules do not cover as much space as a coarse sand-grain.' This enables us to estimate the diameter of these little animals (probably bacteria) at $2-3\mu$. In another letter he estimates them as having the size of only 1/1,000,000,000th of a coarse sand-grain, which would make them approximately 1μ in diameter. The resolving power of his microscopes was therefore great enough to see an object of this diameter.

The 'counter'

Leeuwenhoek not only measured objects hitherto invisible, but on October 4th, 1677, he also estimated their number by means of a 'counter' (See Plate 4). He sucked up a quantity 'as large as a grain of millet' into a capillary tube, and divided this into '25–30 or more parts.' By counting the Infusoria present in a part, he could compute the number in the whole, and so he became the inventor of the principle on which the modern counting-chamber is made.

CHAPTER THREE

Leeuwenhoek, the Father
of Microbiology

In 1875, the famous microbiologist Christian Gottfried
Ehrenberg appealed to the scientists of the world to celebrate
the bicentenary of Leeuwenhoek's discovery of the Protozoa;
there was support from many countries but not from England
where Leeuwenhoek had been so highly esteemed during his
lifetime. Afterwards it was discovered that Ehrenberg's cele-
bration was a little late, for Leeuwenhoek's very first description of the Protozoa was found to be in a letter written
not in 1675, but in the previous year (his sixth letter in *Phil.
Trans.* IX, pp. 179–182, dated September 7th, 1674).

In this letter he wrote: 'About two hours distant from this
town (Delft) lies an inland lake, called the Berkelse Meer,
whose bottom in places is very marshy or boggy. In winter
its water is very clear, but at the beginning or in the middle
of summer it becomes whitish, and there are then little
green clouds floating through it; which, according to the
saying of the country folk living there, is caused by the dew,
which happens to fall at that time and which they call
"honey-dew". . . . Passing just lately over this lake . . . and
seeing the water as above described, I took a little of it in
a glass phial; and examining this water next day, I found
floating in it divers earthy particles, and some green streaks,
spirally wound serpent-wise, and orderly arranged after the
manner of copper or tin worms which distillers use to cool

their liquors as they distil over. The whole circumference of each of these streaks was about the thickness of a hair of one's head (a). Among these there were, besides, very many little animalcules (b), whereof some were roundish, while others, a bit bigger, consisted of an oval. On these last I saw two little legs near the head and two little fins at the hindmost end of the body (c). Others were somewhat longer than an oval, and these were very slow in moving and few in number (d). These animalcules had divers colours, some being whitish and transparent; others with green and glittering little scales; others again were green in the middle, and before and behind white; others yet were ashen grey. And the motion of most of these animalcules in the water was so swift, and so various, upwards, downwards, and roundabouts, that it was wonderful to see: and I judge that some of these little creatures were above a thousand times smaller than the smallest ones I have ever yet seen, upon the rind of cheese, in wheaten flour, mould, and the like' (e).

This passage has been overlooked by most protozoologists, but Schill (1887) and Dobell, in his classical book (1932), reprinted this passage, which contains, as the microbiologist Kluyver says, 'Nothing less than the *discovery of microscopic beings.*' Dobell believes (a) to be *Spirogyra*, (b) some Protozoa, (c) probably Rotifers, (d) probably Ciliates, and (e) mites. It is interesting to note that in this first description Leeuwenhoek had already tried to measure these organisms.'

The famous 'Leeuwenhoek letter'

Very soon followed the famous Leeuwenhoek letter dated October 9th, 1676 (New Style—see note 5): 'Concerning little animals observed by Mr Antoni van Leeuwenhoek in Rain, Well, Sea, and Snow-water; and also in water wherein Pepper had lain infused.' This very long letter is written in an unusual form. At the end of it he remarks that 'these my observations are taken from my diary which I keep from time to time'; accordingly we find that Leeuwenhoek generally gives the observations, in the order in which they were made, without any attempt to summarize or correlate them. This makes the famous letter very difficult to read, but it does enable the sequence of the observations to be followed.

In his masterly book *The Life of Science* Sarton says of Leonardo da Vinci, 'He wrote them (i.e. his notes) for his own private use; it is almost as if we heard him think, as if we were admitted to the secret laboratory where his discoveries were slowly maturing. Such an opportunity is unique in the history of science.' This is also applicable in the present case; Leeuwenhoek wrote to Constantijn Huygens: 'I have couched my observations in the form of a journal, merely that they be better credited in England and elsewhere.' In his notes Leonardo da Vinci turned many times to the reader, so that his notes were evidently not for his private use alone; Leeuwenhoek wrote in one of his first letters to the Royal Society (August 15th, 1673): 'I beg you and the Gentlemen under whose eyes this happens to come to bear in mind that my observations and opinions are only the result of my own impulse and curiosity and that there are in this town no amateurs who, like me, dabble in this art. Take my simple pen, my boldness and my opinions for what they are; they follow without any particular order.' He speaks to the reader and asks his opinion, just as Leonardo da Vinci did.

The beginning of the famous letter is very characteristic; Leeuwenhoek mentions all the circumstances under which he made his observations, 'In the year 1675, about half-way through September, . . . I discovered living creatures in rain, which had stood but a few days in a new tub, that was painted blue within. This observation provoked me to investigate this water more narrowly; and especially because these animals were, to my eye, more than ten thousand times smaller than the animalcule which Swammerdam has portrayed and called by the name of Water-louse, which you can see alive and moving in the water with the naked eye.*

'Of the first sort that I discovered in the said water, I saw, after divers observations, that the bodies consisted of 5, 6, 7, or 8 clear globules†, but without being able to discern any membrane of skin that held these globules together, or in which they were enclosed. When these animalcules bestirred themselves, they sometimes stuck out two little horns‡, which continually moved, after the fashion of a horse's ears. The part between these little horns was flat, their body else being roundish, save only that it ran somewhat to a point at the hind end; at which pointed end it had a tail, near four times as long as the whole body and looking as thick, when viewed through my microscope, as a spider's web. At the end of this tail was a pellet, of the bigness of one of the globules of the body; and this tail I could not perceive to be used by them for their movements in very clear water. These little animals were the most wretched creatures that I have ever seen; for when with the pellet they did hit on any particles or little filaments (of which there are many in the water, especially if it has but stood some days) they stuck entangled in them; and then pulled their body out into an oval, and did struggle, by strongly stretching themselves, to get their tail loose; whereby their whole body then sprang back towards the pellet of the tail, and their tails then coiled up serpent-wise, after the fashion of a copper or iron wire that, having been wound close about a round stick and then taken off, kept all its windings. This motion of stretching out and pulling together of the tail continued; and I have seen several hundreds of animalcules, caught fast by one another in a few filaments, lying within the compass of a coarse grain of sand.'

From this admirable description it is obvious that Leeuwenhoek had observed a species of *Vorticella*. He saw the

* This Water-louse is thought to be the Cladoceran, *Daphnia*.
† Vacuoles.
‡ The cilia round the peristome.

cilia round the peristome but not until 1713 did he discover the function of these 'vibrissae.' He thought that *Vorticella* was a swimming animal, but in 1713 he corrected this mistake, for, having discovered the muscle in the stalk (=tail), he described it and the method of contraction. As he had seen the spirally twisted chloroplast of *Spirogyra*, and afterwards found the spiral structure of the cell wall in wood fibres, and saw spirals in muscle cells, he quite naturally thought that the spiral was one of the best forms of construction found in Nature.

It is understandable that Leeuwenhoek should have been inclined to recognize the same parts of the body in the microscopical creatures discovered by him as in the greater animals around him. At the beginning of the nineteenth century we find Ehrenberg, the best protozoologist of his time, making the same attempt to draw parallels between unicellular and multicellular creatures. Often the word 'globule' means a cell, but in the letter quoted above it evidently refers to a vacuole.

It is quite impossible to quote in full the descriptions of the other animalcules which Leeuwenhoek found living in his water-butt, but it is very interesting to follow him in his further observations. He thought that the animalcules lived in rain-drops and so made his Observation II: 'May 26th, 1676, it rained very hard; the rain growing less, I caused some of that rain-water running down from a slated roof, to be gathered in a clean glass, after it had been washed two or three times with the water. And in this I observed some few little creatures, and seeing them I thought they might have been produced in the leaden-gutters in some water that might in there have remained before.' His critical mind now caused him to make Observation III: 'On the same day, the rain continuing, I took a great porcelain dish and exposed it to the free air in my courtyard upon a wooden vessel, about a foot and a half high, so that no earthy parts, from the falling of the rain-water upon that place, might be spattered or dashed into the said dish. With the first water that fell into the dish I washed it (and the glass in which I was to keep the water) very clean and then flung the water away and received fresh into it, but could discern no living creatures therein.'

He kept the water a few days and observed it on May 30th and 31st and perceived 'very few, exceedingly small animals,' and 'comparing them with a cheese mite, I make the proportion of one of these small water creatures to a cheese mite, to be like that of a bee to a horse; for the circumference of one of these little animals in water, is not so big as the thickness of a hair in a cheese mite' ($1-3\mu$). 'And I imagine, that ten hundred thousand of these little creatures do not equal an ordinary grain of sand in bigness.' One can imagine that Oldenburg in his translation in the *Philosophical Transactions* spoke of 'living atoms,' a term not used by Leeuwenhoek. It is not quite clear what creature Leeuwenhoek saw but Dobell considers it was a *Monas*; he thinks that a sand-grain here means a coarse sand-grain, so that the diameter of the animalcule would be about $8 \cdot 7\mu$. If we believe that it was a fine sand-grain, the diameter would have been about $2 \cdot 5\mu$. Leeuwenhoek continued his observations on rain-water, and then made some on river-water, on water from his well, and on sea-water from the shore at Scheveningen: in all these types of water he discovered animalcules.

Pepper-water

Now comes a very interesting passage, which begins as follows: 'Having several times endeavoured to discover the cause of the pungency of *Pepper* upon our tongue (and that the rather, because it has been found, that though the pepper had lain a whole year in vinegar, yet it retained its pungency) I put about one-third of an ounce of whole pepper in water, placing it in my study, with the sole design thereby that the pepper being rendered soft I might be enabled the better to observe what I proposed to myself. This pepper having lain three weeks in the water, to which I had twice added some snow-water (the other water being exhaled) I looked upon it the 24th of April, 1676, and discerned in it to my great wonder, an incredible number of very little animals of divers kind.'

The mechanistic theory of taste

[One might wonder why Leeuwenhoek laid pepper in snow-water and this requires a short explanation. Snow-water, kept in well-stoppered glass bottles in the cellar for sometimes three or more years was the most pure water in olden times. As for the matter of the pungency of pepper, one has to understand Leeuwenhoek's theory on the reason for the difference in taste of, for instance, sugar and salt. In his letter of August 14th, 1673, he gives his opinion, in accordance with the mechanistic theories of his time: 'To illustrate this, I shall here speak of the difference of the taste between salt and sugar. The grain of sugar consists of divers pointed and angular small figures: and yet angular and pointed as these figures are, they would not, if they remained entire, cause any taste upon our Tongue, for as much as (with submission to better judgement) their angles and points are big: each point or angle of these grains of sugar not touching one or two globules of our tongue, but comprising a great number of them, and that the rather because I take it for granted, that a single globule (of which bodies the pointed protuberances of our tongue are made up) is many thousand times smaller than a common grain of sand, and therefore can produce no taste. . . . But, sugar is a body dissoluble in water . . . wherefore that substance, when put upon the tongue, is dissolved by the moisture and warmth it meets there, and so proves even smooth and soft upon the tongue, affecting it with pleasure. But salt, on the contrary, though it dissolves in water as to its great parts, yet retains some rigid small particles, which by warmth, when they are taken upon the tongue, grow yet more rigid, and are so subtile, that they *prick* the globules of our tongue, though not so stiff, that they *wound* them.' Leeuwenhoek thought that the finest particles of pepper would be sharp little needles, as he had found in the sap of *Arum*, causing pain on his tongue (bundles of raphides, which he discovered and described in his twelfth letter, see page 175). When the pepper was made soft in the water, he expected to see the needles, which in his opinion were the cause of the pungency. It was like Saul, who tried to find his ass and found a kingdom!

The birthday of Bacteriology

In his infusion of pepper Leeuwenhoek found four different kinds of little animals; the first three he described were Protozoa, but: 'The fourth sort of creatures, which moved through the three former sorts were incredibly small, and so small in my eye, that I judged, that if a hundred of them lay stretched out one by another, they would not equal the *length* of a coarse grain of sand (870μ); and according to this estimate ten hundred thousand of them could not equal the dimensions of a grain of such coarse sand.' The Dutch microbiologist, Kluyver, says: 'The measures given leave no doubt that he observed bacteria here; consequently this is the first unmistakable description of representatives of this group of organisms, and there is every reason to consider the 24th April, 1676, as the birthday of Bacteriology.'

Leeuwenhoek repeated his experiment on April 26th, May 26th, June 14th, August 2nd, and many other times. In the infusion made on August 2nd he 'saw in the afternoon, about three o'clock on August 6th, very distinctly little eels or worms, lying huddled together and wriggling, just as if you saw with your naked eye a whole tubful of very little eels and water, the eels moving about in swarms; and the whole

E

seemed to be alive with the multitudinous animalcules. For me this was among all the marvels that I discovered in nature the most marvellous of all, and I must say, that for my part, no more pleasant sight has met my eye than this of so many thousands of living creatures in one small drop of water, all huddling and moving, but each creature having its own motion. And even if I said that there were a hundred-thousand animalcules in one drop of water which I took from the surface of the water, I should not err. Others seeing this would estimate the number at quite ten times more, of which I have instances, but I give the lowest numbers. My method for seeing the very smallest animalcules and eels do I not impart to others, nor that for seeing very many animalcules all at the same time, but keep that for myself alone.' This vivid description of *Spirillum* clearly showing how delighted Leeuwenhoek was at this discovery, poses for us the problem of his method of observation, which has already been discussed in the previous chapter.

Continuing his observations he saw 'a multitude of straight little tubes . . . even four or five times shorter than the aforesaid little eels or worms'; these smaller ones must undoubtedly have been bacteria. He experimented with his 'little eels' by putting a little vinegar into some pepper-water. He invariably saw that 'as soon as the pepper-water was mixed with the vinegar, the animalcules that were in the pepper-water died instantly, without my being able to perceive that the little eels which were in the vinegar suffered any hurt from the pepper-water.' Leeuwenhoek gave his observations on the procreation of the 'vinegar eels' (*Anguillula*) and discovered the viviparity of these animals, then gave a description of the structure of pepper-corns, where he observed the 'minute particles with their sides usually flat, but in many places with projecting angles and bumps' (the polyhedric cells). Next he described the structure of wheat and then the structure of ginger and the animalcules he

66

observed after laying the roots of ginger in snow-water. He also gave a short passage on the influences of spices on the digestion (he thought that spices contained sharp parts, thus 'causing a pungent taste for some time') and he made infusions of cloves in rain-water and well-water, and of nutmeg in well-water. He then said: 'It has several times been put forwards against me, that there are extraordinary little animalcules in the air, which are hidden from our eyes, and which can be discerned only by means of excellent magnifying glasses or telescopes and which have been seen in Rome.' This remark may refer to Athanasius Kircher (1602–1680), one of the first people to use the microscope in tracing the cause of diseases, who observed the 'vermiculae' in the blood of patients suffering from plague. It is almost certain that Kircher could not see bacteria with his glasses. Leeuwenhoek says: 'I will not deny that there may be living creatures in the air, which are so small as to escape our sight; I only say that I have not seen them. Nor do I believe that they may be able to remain alive in the air about our horizon (this means perhaps the layers of air close to the earth) but rather that they would be formed in the clouds and could remain alive there in the continual dampness.'

Leeuwenhoek was aware that he was opening up a new field: 'These observations concerning living creatures in the above mentioned liquids, require indeed closer attention and description, but that whole also requires a whole man which my circumstances do not allow of, and I have employed only my spare time upon them.' This shows that his post was not a sinecure.

Oldenburg wrote to Leeuwenhoek to ask him 'to acquaint us with his method of observing, that others may confirm such observations.' Leeuwenhoek gave his method of using the 'counter' (see Chapter Two) in his letter of March 19th, 1677, and again on October 5th, 1677. As Dobell says, 'The disbelievers did a signal service to posterity for they put

67

Leeuwenhoek on his mettle and thereby enabled us to read today a detailed record of some of the most remarkable and original researches ever executed.' Leeuwenhoek added the attestations of eight eye-witnesses, among them Alexander Petrie, the Pastor of the English Congregation in Delft, to his continued observations, writing amongst other things in his letter of January 4th, 1678: 'I did fill a small clean glass with pounded pepper to one-third of its height, adding two-thirds of rainwater, . . . within thrice twenty-four hours I discovered in it so great a many of such inconceivably small creatures, that a man's mind may not contain them all. In my judgement . . . they were much more than a thousand times thinner than a hair of one's head, and three or four times as long as thick.'

The disbelief of the Royal Society

In the meantime, the Royal Society tried to repeat Leeuwenhoek's experiments. In Birch's *History of the Royal Society* is a vivid account of the meetings at that time. At the meeting in November, 1677, 'there were produced a great many exceeding small and thin pipes of glass of various sizes,' but the Fellows could not see the little animals, so it was therefore ordered, 'that against the next meeting pepper-water should be provided, and some better microscopes than the one made use of, that the truth of Mr. Leeuwenhoek's assertions might, if possible, be experimentally examined.' On the 8th of November, 1677, 'the first thing exhibited was the experiment charged on Mr Hooke at the last meeting, of examining pepper-water with better microscopes and thinner and smaller pipes.' This experiment was not satisfactory and so at the following meeting the experiments were continued.

On November 15th, it became apparent that Leeuwenhoek was right: 'The first experiment there exhibited was the pepper-water, which had been made with rain-water and a small quantity of common black pepper put whole into it about nine or ten days before. In this Mr Hooke had all the week discovered great numbers of exceedingly small animals swimming to and fro. They appeared of the bigness of a mite through a glass that magnified about a hundred thousand times in bulk (about 450 times). . . . They were seen by many of the Fellows so that there was no longer any doubt of Mr Leeuwenhoek's discovery.'

Hooke stated 'some of these little animals are so exceedingly small that millions of millions might be contained in one drop of water.' He also wrote to Leeuwenhoek himself; Dobell has published the draft of this letter which is in the possession of the Royal Society. 'Of this the President and all the members present were satisfied and it seems wonderful that there should be such an infinite number of animals in so imperceptible quantity of matter. That these animals should be so perfectly shaped and indeed with such curious organs of motion as to be able to move nimbly, to turn, stay, accelerate and retard their progress at pleasure. And it was not less surprising to find that these were gygantick monsters in comparison of the lesser sort which almost filled the water.' As Dobell remarks, it seems likely that these 'gygantick monsters' were Protozoa, while those of the lesser sort were bacteria.

Hooke also wrote: 'His Majesty (King Charles II, founder and patron of the Royal Society) was desirous to see them (the animalcules) and was very pleased with the observation and mentioned your name at the same time.' A friend of Leeuwenhoek's translated 'mentioned' as 'mentioned with great respect,' an expression which Leeuwenhoek was very pleased to hear!

Leeuwenhoek's discovery, which was at first hardly credited, was now fully recognized. It has been said that 'when Leeuwenhoek's own mind tried to direct, he could produce nothing but chaos,' and again, that when others praised him, this could only 'be ascribed to an insufficient knowledge of his works and of those of his contemporaries.' By quoting many of his letters verbatim, it can be seen that this is not wholly justified; Leeuwenhoek's work was often highly original, and carried out in the face of opposition from his contemporaries. It is also clear that, in spite of views to the contrary, Leeuwenhoek was undoubtedly the discoverer of the Protozoa, bacteria, and Rotifers. It is impossible to describe in detail all his discoveries, so only the more important ones will be dealt with, and for the sake of clarity his observations will not always be mentioned in chronological order.

The structure of the animalcules and of water

When we enquire into Leeuwenhoek's ideas on the structure of the little animals we reach the conclusion that he believed their structure to be identical with that of the 'higher' animals. He wrote to Constantijn Huygens (20th May, 1679): 'I have often let my thoughts run on the extreme small vessels and sinews wherewith the very little animalcules are furnished withal; . . . and that these little animals, on which I can discern no feet, must notwithstanding be furnished with instruments for motion; and that these instruments must consist, in part, of blood vessels which convey nourishment into them, and of sinews which move them; and that through these vessels, moreover, water must also pass. And this being so, we must suppose the particles of the water itself to be so small as to be for us inconceivable: and I am persuaded that no man will ever advance so far in science as to be able to gaze upon the particles whereof water itself consists.' As we have already mentioned, the famous Ehrenberg in 1838 described the Protozoa as 'perfect animals' with one or more stomachs, so it is no wonder that Leeuwenhoek, who was the first to see them, thought that their organization was the same as that of the animals with which he was more familiar. He often says that 'foreseeing Nature follows in all cases the same way,' a unitarian concept which he continued to hold all his life.

The propagation of the animalcules

In his letter of 9th November, 1695, he wrote: 'One day afterwards I looked at the animalcules again and saw to my wonder that many of them were coupled, some of them even coupled before my eye; and at the beginning of their copulation they had a wobbling motion, but after coupling they swam forward together, and did stay still too, fixed to the glass.' And again: 'After observing what I have just related (namely, that there are animalcules which do not take to swimming about until they have reached their full growth, and which soon after are ready to copulate; and there withal that a full grown animalcule is produced in one night) I was now, to my great satisfaction, delivered from those difficulties, that I had for years laboured under, concerning the generation of these little creatures.' In his letter of 7th March, 1692, he had already written, 'I did perceive a plenty of these little animalcules, which were coupled together, and so long remained in this posture: and I observed how the bigger sort dragged the little ones along, or swam forward with them, with the help of very plenteous feet, wherewith these animals are furnished withal; so that I was able on this occasion to observe the copulation of these little animals clearer than ever before.' Dobell says that in his opinion, the foregoing passage is of great interest, since it is evidently a record of observations made upon the conjugation and fission of Ciliates. He considers that one animal swimming along with another must have been a conjugation pair, whereas one organism trailing another behind it must really have been dividing transversely into two.

Bacteria in the mouth

The most famous passage describing bacteria (which had been discovered in 1676) is to be found in his letter of 17th September, 1683: 'I am in the habit of rubbing my teeth in the morning, and then swill out my mouth with water; and often after eating, to clean my back teeth with a tooth-pick, as well as rubbing them hard with a cloth, wherefore my teeth back and front remain as clean and white that only a few people of my age (fifty-one) can compare with me. Also when I rub my gums with hard salt, they will not bleed. Yet all this does not make my teeth so clean but that I can see, looking at them with a hollow mirror, that something will stick and grow between some of the molars and teeth, a little white matter, as thick as batter. Observing it I judged that although I could not see anything moving in it there were yet living animalcules in it. I then mixed it several times with pure rain-water, in which there were no animalcules, and also with saliva that I took from my mouth after eliminating the air bubbles lest these should stir the spittle. I then again and again saw that there were many small living animalcules in the said matter, which moved very prettily.' He then gives a description of four different sorts of bacteria, namely a mobile rod-like bacterium (A), *Selenomonas sputigerum* (B), *Pseudomonas* (E) and *Leptothrix buccalis* (F). (See Plate 5.)

This observation is wrongly considered by many writers to be the discovery of bacteria, but Leeuwenhoek's letter of 1683 contains the first drawings of them. He was not content with these first observations so he examined the 'tartar' from the mouths of people of different ages and sexes. The first persons to be examined were 'two different women, who, I am convinced, dayly cleaned their mouths.' (No doubt he refers to his second wife, Cornelia Swalmius, and to his daughter Maria.) He found the little animals again, and then extended his investigation to include people whom he sus-

72

pected of not cleaning their mouths as well as he and the members of his family were wont to do. He found the animalcules again between the teeth of a child, and then experimented on himself. 'I did not clean my mouth on purpose for three days and then took the matter that had stuck to the gum above the front teeth . . . and discovered a few living animalcules in it.' Again he says: 'While an old man (who leads a sober life and never drinks brandy or tobacco, and very seldom wine) was talking to me, my eye fell upon his teeth which were all coated over; this made me ask him when he had last cleaned his mouth and the reply was, that he had never washed his mouth all his life. . . . I took the matter that stuck between and against his teeth, and on mixing it with clean water . . . I observed an incredible number of living animalcules swimming more nimbly than

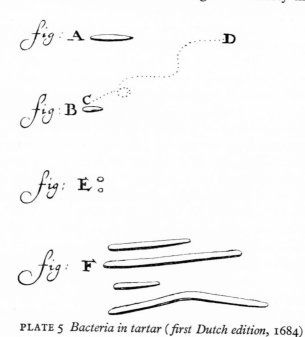

PLATE 5 *Bacteria in tartar (first Dutch edition, 1684)*

I had ever seen up to this time. The big sort which were very plentiful bent their bodies into curves while going forward, as in fig. G.' Dobell says that 'G' is unquestionably a Spirochaete and Kluyver thinks that it may be *Spirillum*. (It is interesting to see that this figure is present in all editions of Leeuwenhoek's works except in the first Dutch edition!) Leeuwenhoek continues: 'I also took the spittle and the white matter lodged upon and between his teeth from an old man who is in the habit of taking aqua vitae in the morning and of drinking wine and tobacco in the afternoon, wondering whether the little animals could live in spite of this continual drinking. I judged this man, because his teeth were so uncommonly dirty, would not clean his mouth; when I asked him, he answered: never in all my life with water but every day by flushing it with aqua vitae and wine. . . . In the matter which I had taken from between his front teeth (for he had not a back tooth in his mouth) I saw many . . . animalcules, consisting of two of the smallest sort.

'Furthermore I took some strong wine vinegar into my mouth, set my teeth, and let the vinegar run between them several times; after this I rinsed three times with clean water. I then once more took some of the foresaid matter both from my front teeth and from my grinders, mixing it with spittle as well as clean rain-water; nearly always I discovered an incredible number of living animalcules, but mostly in the matter which I took from between my back teeth. . . . I also mixed a little wine vinegar with the mingled spittle and with the water; the animals therein died at once. From this I drew the conclusion that the vinegar which I had in my mouth did not penetrate through all the matter which was firmly lodged between and against my teeth, and only killed those animalcules that were in the outermost parts of the white matter. . . .'

He concludes: 'There are more animals living in the unclean matter on the teeth in one's mouth than there are men in a whole Kingdom, especially in those who never clean their mouths, owing to which such a stench comes from the mouth of many that one can hardly bear talking to them. Many call this a stenching breath, but actually it is in most cases a stinking mouth.

'I imagined that I could discern as many as a thousand living little animals in a quantity of this matter no bigger than one hundredth part of a sand-grain.' These quoted passages give a vivid impression of Leeuwenhoek's methods, of his curiosity and his experiments. As A. W. Meyer has pointed out (1937), Leeuwenhoek was truly an 'experimental biologist'—he produced 'order' and not 'chaos.'

Anaerobic bacteria

In his letter of June 14th, 1680, Leeuwenhoek describes an experiment on anaerobic or semi-aerobic bacteria: 'When it became known to me, that divers opinions have been expressed concerning the generation of little animals; and as I heard, especially, that a certain Gentleman (this was doubtless Francesco Redi) has written that no living creature can be generated if the vessel, or bottle, in which any moisture or meat has been put, be tightly stoppered; I had a mind to carry out some trials of this matter. Accordingly I took two glass tubes, which after having been closed at the bottom, were filled (to the half) with pounded pepper, and then (to two-thirds) with clean rain-water, as soon as it had been collected in a clean china dish (in which no victuals had been put for quite ten years); then, by the heat of a flame, the glass was fashioned so as to have a small opening at its pointed end; after a lapse of about the quarter of an hour, I sealed the aperture tight by means of the flame. I also prepared myself a second glass, treating it likewise, save that in this I left the aperture at the top open, in order to ascertain, if possible, in which water the living animalcules would first turn up.' (Plate 6).

75

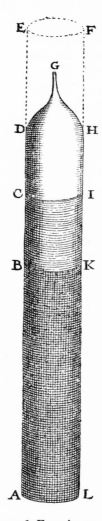

PLATE 6 *Experiment on
anaerobic bacteria*

After it had stood thus for three days, 'I took a little water out of the second glass, and discovered a great many very little animals. . . . Breaking the first tube (after five days) the water escaped with force out of the tube: for which reason I rather fancied there would be no living creatures in this water. But I found the contrary. . . . I perceived in it . . . many sorts of living animalcules . . . still, I bethought me, that when the Gentleman aforesaid spoke of living creatures, he meant only worms or maggots, which you commonly see in rotten meat and which ordinarily proceed from eggs of flies, and which are so big that we have no need of a good microscope to describe them.' As the great Dutch bacteriologist Beyerinck pointed out, the animalcules which Leeuwenhoek discovered were undoubtedly not Protozoa but bacteria, *Bacillus coli*, *Azotobacter*, and *Amylobacter saccharobutyricum*; he also pointed out that these are the earliest observations on any anaerobic bacteria. Dobell, writing on these observations, comments, 'it seems remarkable that Leeuwenhoek—always a vigorous opponent of the doctrine of spontaneous generation—appears to have made no further study of the very interesting phenomena which the foregoing experiments record . . . he probably imagined that the rainwater (containing their "seeds") introduced into the sealed tube animalcules or "seeds".'

Leeuwenhoek discovered his bacteria in the mouths of healthy people, so it is no wonder that he never thought that bacteria could be the cause of illness.

Entozoic animalcules

In the same year as he described the free-living Protozoa, he described (in his letter of October 19th, 1674) in the bile of a cow 'some corpuscles, which to my eye, looked as big as ant eggs'; these may have been the eggs of parasitic Trematode worms. He also saw in 'the bile from three old rabbits very many oval corpuscles' which Dobell takes to be oocysts 77 of the Protozoan *Eimeria stiedae*, though Swellengrebel thinks that these were eggs of *Fasciola hepatica*. Leeuwenhoek also described (letter of November 12th, 1680) 'animals a good ten times thicker (than a spermatozoon) in the thin matter that was in the fly's guts, and moved forward very quickly.' This description would support the idea that he saw *Crithidia* or *Leptomonas*. Leeuwenhoek also found living animalcule in his own excrement. The letter of November 4th, 1681, opens in his characteristic style: 'I weigh about 160 pounds and have been very nigh the same way for some thirty years, and I have ordinarily of a morning a well-formed stool; but now and then hitherto I have a looseness . . . when I went to stool some two, three or four times a day. But this summer this befell me very often, and especially when I partook of hot smoked beef, that was a bit fat, or ham, which food I am very fond of. . . . My excrement being so thin I was at divers times persuaded to examine it. . . . I will only say, that I have generally seen, in my excrement . . . animalcules a-moving very prettily; some of them a bit bigger, others a bit less, than a blood globule, but all of one and the same make. Their bodies were somewhat longer than broad, and their belly, which was flat-like, furnished with sundry little paws, wherewith they made such a stir in the clear medium, and among the globules, that you might even fancy that you saw a woodlouse running up against a wall. . . . I have also seen a sort of animalcules that had a figure of our river eels; these were in very great plenty and so withal, that I deemed 500 or 600 of them laid out end to end would not reach to the length of a full-grown eel such as there are in vinegar. These had a very nimble motion and bent their bodies serpent-wise and shot through the stuff as quick as a pike does through the water.'

The first animalcules are thought by Dobell to be *Giardia intestinalis*; of the second, he says 'it can hardly be doubted that these organisms were spirochaetes. . . . This is the first record of their occurrence.' It has been stated that this passage shows Leeuwenhoek suffered from dysentery, caused by *Balantidium coli*, but Dobell considers that 'beyond all doubt, this is a literary fiction lacking all foundation.' It is, however, remarkable that Leeuwenhoek did not associate the presence of the entozoic animalcules with disease. He found another entozoic animalcule in the intestine of the frog (probably *Trichomonas batrachorum*), and others (*Opalina* and other Protozoa) in the faeces; as the frogs were healthy and lively, there was in this case no reason to associate the presence of the animalcules with any disease.

Reproduction by fission

Leeuwenhoek solved yet another problem in the later years of his life. In a letter dated February 5th, 1705, he gave a description of the 'iron-flagellate' (*Antiphysa*). He was interested in them 'especially because their colour was like that of oaken wood, and in many places they were encrusted with little granules, just as if they were made up of congealed, round particles' (of ferric oxide). At the ends of the twigs were 'rosette-like structures which seem to consist of several globules. . . . During this observation I saw one of the four globules break off and make off as though swimming away.' Here Leeuwenhoek saw the propagation of a colonial phyto-flagellate. In his last letter on Protozoa (November 5th, 1716) he describes the multiplication of another phytoflagellate, *Polytoma*. The 'animalcules lived for no longer than thirty to thirty-six hours, and then they fixed themselves upon the glass, while soon after, their body burst asunder, and lay divided into eight portions. This makes 262,144 animals in four days.' All these observations tend to show that Leeuwenhoek not only anticipated the future of microbiology but as Cole said, he 'must be regarded as the father of Protozoology.'

CHAPTER FOUR

Leeuwenhoek and the Theory of Generation: the Discovery of Spermatozoa

History of the problem—Aristotle

The problem of generation or propagation has puzzled mankind from the dawn of history onwards; in the early days, no microscopical or anatomical observations were made, so recourse was had to philosophical speculations. For centuries, even up till the time of Leeuwenhoek himself, the theories of Aristotle were universally supported. These ideas may be briefly summarized as follows:

'Some animals are formed as a result of the union of male and female . . . among the Sanguinea (=Vertebrates), with few exceptions, the creature, when its growth is complete, is either male or female . . . yet some bloodless animals generate indeed, but not offspring of the same kind; such are all that come into being, not from a union of the sexes, but from decaying earth and excrements. . . . The male and female principles may be put down first and foremost as origins of generation, the former as containing the efficient cause of generation, the latter the material of it. . . . Now as a matter of fact such parts are in the female the so-called uterus, in the male the testes and the penis. . . . We find that some Sanguinea have no testes at all, as the classes of fish and of serpents, but only two spermatic ducts' (note—these are, in fact, testes). ' . . . The reason why the uterus is always internal, although the testes are sometimes external, is that in it is contained the egg or foetus, which needs guarding, shelter, and maturation by concoction.' (Aristotle thought that this 'concoction' took place by means of the vital heat—*calor innatus*—which comes from the heart.)

Aristotle then discusses whether the semen comes from all parts of the body or not. He says, 'The resemblance of children to parents is no proof that the semen comes from the whole body, because the resemblance is found also in voice, nails, hair, and way of moving, from which nothing comes. And men generate before they yet have certain characters, such as a beard or grey hair. We may also ask whether the semen comes from each of the homogeneous parts only, such as flesh and bone and sinew, or also from the heterogeneous, such as face and hands.' Aristotle's answer is, 'If there were anything drawn from the whole of a word, it would be drawn from each of the syllables also, and this of course means that it would be drawn from each of the letters, plus the assemblage of them together. . . . If the semen is drawn from all the parts of both parents alike, we shall have two animals formed, for the semen will contain all the parts of each of them.' So Aristotle concludes: 'Without the assemblage of the parts there would be no resemblance . . . if the parts of the body are scattered about the semen, how do they live? If they were connected with each other, then surely they would be a tiny animal. . . . The parts cannot remain sound and living if (as Empedocles thought) they are "torn asunder" from each other when small, any more than they can when they are fully grown. . . . So we must say the opposite of what the ancients said; for whereas they said that the semen comes from all the body, we shall say it is that whose nature is to be distributed to the whole of the body. . . . We have previously stated that the final nutriment is the blood, in the Sanguinea . . . since the semen

81

F

is also a secretion of the nutriment, and that in its final stage
it follows that it will be either blood, that which is analogous
to blood, or something formed from this. But since it is from
the blood, when concocted and somehow divided up, that
each part of the body is made, and since the semen if properly
concocted is of quite a different character from the blood
when it is separated from it . . . therefore it is plain that
semen will be a secretion of the nutriment when reduced to
blood, being that which is finally distributed to the parts of
the body. . . . So that the semen which is to form the hand or
the face or the whole animal is already the hand or face or
the whole animal undifferentiated; what each of them is
actually, such is the semen *potentially*. . . . Neither the hand
nor any other part of the body whatsoever is not hand or
other part in a true sense if it be without soul or some other
power. . . .

'The soul forms the body . . . not all parts are formed
simultaneously. And the part which must of necessity be
formed first is the one which possesses the principle of
growth. . . . Thus, if the heart is formed first in certain
animals . . . we may suppose that it is the heart which
supplies the principle. . . . The semen contains a good deal
of hot air in it, because of the internal heat. . . . The reason
for the whiteness of the semen is that it is a foam. . . . The
male supplies the soul, the female the nourishment; the parts
(or the whole organism) are potentially, not actually, in the
seed; the parts cannot be loose, for then there would be
chaos; only in the semen are there the potential parts, for if
they were also in the menstruum there would be two young;
the male is hotter and therefore his blood is better concocted,
the female is "a damaged male".' The passages quoted above
provide a rough summary of the views of Aristotle on the
problem of generation. For centuries these were the domin-
ant theories, although some independent scholars, such as
Paracelsus, enunciated the theory that half of the semen

came from the female and half from the male. In 1651, however, William Harvey published his famous *Exercitationes de Generatione Animalium*, a book which brought the reproduction of animals to the attention of scientists; this became one of the topics of the day, and marked the beginning of a struggle between the theories of epigenesis and preformation.

Epigenesis and preformation

The theory of *epigenesis* embodied the idea that organs were formed successively, while the theory of *preformation* asserted nothing that was not in the egg can originate from the egg; a thing *is*, or *is not*, so that when a young animal comes out of an egg, it must have been inside it all the time. The whole idea of development is a very difficult one; it is more than 'not being' and less than 'being,' so it is no wonder that many investigators rejected the idea held by the epigeneticists of a potential being.

Harvey proved himself a follower of Aristotle, and sums up his own ideas in the dictum *Omne vivum ex ovo* (all animals come from the egg), though he did not abandon the idea of spontaneous generation for some of the lower animals. The higher animals are evolved by epigenesis, the lower by metamorphosis, or a complete reconstruction of rudimentary organs, as exemplified by the development of the insect pupa; Harvey in fact shares Aristotle's belief that the pupa is the insect's egg! The influence of the sperm on the development of the embryo he believes to be due to the vital force it contains, and this he compares to the secret force of the heavenly bodies upon all life on the earth.

Somewhat later, we have the preformationist ideas of the Italian Malpighi, who studied the development of the chicken; he said, 'the filaments of the chicken (*stamina pulli*) pre-existed in the egg, likewise as the seeds of the plants.' At the same time the Dutch biologists Reinier de Graaf and Swammerdam discovered the 'Graafian follicle' which they believed to be the mammalian egg (1671–72); while de Graaf and Steno suggested the name 'ovary' (the mammalian ovaries were previously called *testes muliebris*). De Graaf rejected Aristotle's opinion that the embryo originates from the male alone, and he thought that the impregnation was caused by an *aura seminalis*, a volatile part of the semen. (Leeuwenhoek was acquainted with de Graaf, who introduced him to the Royal Society, and he certainly knew Swammerdam. It has been said, although without a great deal of evidence, that they were friends during the period when Leeuwenhoek was in Amsterdam.) The attention which was drawn to the egg by the views of de Graaf was renewed by Swammerdam in his famous *Historia generalis* (1669) which was written in Dutch and so was intelligible to Leeuwenhoek.

Swammerdam studied insects particularly, and he demonstrated to the Grand Duke of Tuscany how a 'butterfly could be extracted from a caterpillar' (which was about to undergo metamorphosis!) by a treatment with hot water. It is not necessary to quote all Swammerdam's findings here, but the following summary, taken from Cole, 1930, will give us a sufficient impression of his beliefs. 'The four stages, egg, larva, pupa, imago* are enclosed in that order as in a series of diminishing boxes, and he was consequently beguiled into the belief that generation was not as it appeared, a series of recurring epigenetic cycles, but an unbroken and a continuous process involving the successive emergence, and development by growth, of a series of individuals which had been simultaneously brought into existence at the creation of the world. The doctrine of preformation . . . was in the air, and only required the addition of some fragment of observation to precipitate it as a tangible and attractive hypothesis. The man to achieve this dubious success was Swammerdam.' It is interesting here to note the words of A. W.

84

* imago = adult insect.

Meyer (1939), 'Surprising as it may seem, examination of the literature shows clearly that the doctrine of preformation obtained its chief later support from the outstanding morphological work of such men of science as Malpighi, Swammerdam, Réaumur, and Haller. Except for the supposedly objective, experimental facts obtained by these men, it is unlikely that the words of such philosophers as Malebranche, Leibnitz, and Bonnet would have had such wide influence.' Now the preformationists had to make a choice between two arguments: did the young organism pre-exist in the male or in the female, in the semen or in the egg? As we have seen, the egg was newly discovered, and as the semen was a fluid, with a volatile part, the earlier preformationists were all 'ovulists,' thinking the egg contained the seat of the germ.

Leeuwenhoek's discovery of the spermatozoa

The theories described above were current at the time when Leeuwenhoek was discovering the 'little animals' in water. As we have seen in Chapter Three, he thought that they had structure similar to that of the larger animals, and so to him it was certain that they were born out of 'seeds'—he scorned the idea of spontaneous generation. A. W. Meyer says, 'Leeuwenhoek was not a preformationist,' but he adds, 'his discoveries quite naturally misled him and others as to the role of the spermatozoon.' It will be clear, however, from the following that I regard Leeuwenhoek as a preformationist. In one of his most famous letters (November, 1677), written at the time when the Fellows of the Royal Society were engaged in trying to prove the existence of the 'little animals in pepper-water,' he communicated his discovery of living animals in the semen. This letter was written in Latin; perhaps the delicate nature of the subject furnished a reason for the translation into a language that Leeuwenhoek did not know, or perhaps he wanted to save the secretary this trouble.

85

'I could not feel easy unless I communicated to you the following marvels of nature, convinced that you will grant the liberty I take. After the distinguished Professor Craanen had many times honoured me with a visit, he besought me, in a letter, to demonstrate some of my observations to his kinsman, Mr Ham. On the second occasion when this Mr Ham visited me, he brought with him in a small glass phial the spontaneously discharged semen of a man who was suffering from gonorrhoea, saying that, after a very few minutes (when the matter had become so far liquefied that it could be introduced into a small glass tube), he had seen living animalcules in it, judging these animalcules to have tails, and not to remain alive above twenty-four hours. This gentleman also reported that he had noticed the animalcules were dead after the patient had taken turpentine (a remedy for gonorrhoea). In the presence of Mr Ham, I examined some of this matter which I introduced into a glass tube, and saw some living creatures in it, but when I examined the same matter by myself after the lapse of two or three hours, I observed that they were dead.'

It is clear that Leeuwenhoek gives the priority of this important discovery to Ham, a medical student at Leyden (who was a native of Arnhem and not of Stettin as is sometimes stated). It is also clear that Ham did not understand the importance of his discovery; he thought that the animalcules were the result of the gonorrhoea. Later, Leeuwenhoek quoted a considerable part of this letter, and in the quotation he added, 'which he believed to have arisen by some sort of putrefaction'; I am of the opinion that the translator had omitted these words from the first letter. Leeuwenhoek had, incidentally, seen 'globules' in the semen some years before Ham's observations.

This discovery excited Leeuwenhoek's curiosity, and stimulated him to further independent researches. It is evident that Ham must have had a very good microscope, as he could see the tails of the spermatozoa, so that it was not only the possession of good glasses which gave Leeuwenhoek the superiority; it was his genius! He continued: 'I have divers times examined the same matter (human semen) from a healthy man, not from a sick man, not spoiled by keeping for a long time and not liquefied after the lapse of some time; but immediately after ejaculation before six beats of the pulse had intervened: and I have seen so great a number of living animals in it that sometimes more than a thousand were moving about in an amount of material of the size of a grain of sand. . . . These animalcules were smaller than the corpuscles which impart a red colour to the blood; so that I judge a million of them would not equal in size a large grain of sand. Their bodies which were round, were blunt in front and ran to a point behind. They were furnished with a thin tail, about five or six times as long as the body, and

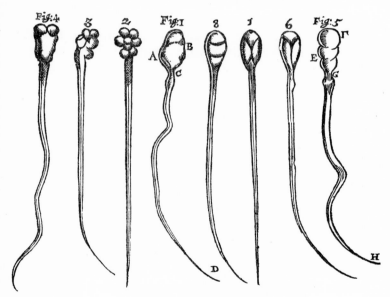

PLATE 7 *Spermatozoa*

very transparent and with the thickness of about one twenty-fifth of the body (Plate 7). They moved forward owing to the motion of their tails like that of a snake or an eel swimming in water; but in the somewhat thicker substance they would have to lash their tails eight or ten times before they could advance a hair's-breadth. I have sometimes fancied that I could even discern different parts on the bodies of these animalcules: but since I have not always been able to do so, I will say no more. Among these animalcules there were also smaller ones, to which I can ascribe nothing but a globular form.

'I remember that some three or four years ago I examined seminal fluid at the request of the late Mr Oldenburg, and that I considered those animalcules to be globules. Yet as I felt averse to make further investigations and still more so from describing them, I did not continue my observations. What I investigate is only what, without sinfully defiling myself, remains as a residue after conjugal coitus. And if your Lordship should consider that these observations may disgust or scandalize the learned, I earnestly beg your Lordship to regard them as private and to publish or destroy them, as your Lordship thinks fit.

'As regards the parts themselves of which the denser substance of the semen is mainly made up, as I have many times observed with wonder, they consist of all manner of great and small vessels, so various and so numerous that I have not the least doubt that they are nerves, arteries and veins. Indeed I have observed these vessels in such great numbers that I felt convinced that in no full-grown human body are there any vessels which cannot be found likewise in sound semen. . . . I conceived that the vessels might perhaps serve for the conveyance of the animal spirits.' As this last paragraph is omitted in the letter of 1698, it seems obvious that Leeuwenhoek no longer believed these observations, and his interpretation of them, to be correct.

From a consideration of the middle portion of Leeuwenhoek's letter written in November, 1677, it is clear that he saw the spermatozoa, measured their numbers, and gave their dimensions fairly correctly; a red blood cell is about 7μ in diameter, the head of the sperm about 6μ in length and its tail about 40μ long and 1μ thick. This is another example of structures which were hitherto invisible, being measured by Leeuwenhoek! This letter also gives us an interesting insight into his psychology; it shows that he was not only an ardent investigator, but also a matter-of-fact person. He felt that he might 'disgust or scandalize' the learned Fellows of the Royal Society, but he felt bound to publish his discoveries and the methods he had used. Fortunately, the Fellows of the Royal Society were not scandalized and the letter was published, in Latin, in their *Transactions*. S. Hoole, when he published the *Select Works of A. van Leeuwenhoek* between 1798 and 1807, omitted all 'passages which to many Readers might be offensive' and so, as Dobell says, this edition of the letters is 'worthless to the student of spermatozoa, all reference to which is carefully castrated.'

Cole (1937) calls attention to the fact that Leeuwenhoek 'undoubtedly regarded the discovery of the spermatozoa as one of his most important. . . . For forty-six years, except for two breaks of five and eight years, he worked and reflected on these germs. They appear in fifty-seven out of his 280 published letters. . . . He examined the spermatozoa of thirty animal types, including eleven Arthropods, two Molluscs, seven fish, one Amphibian, two birds and seven mammals.'

In 1678 Leeuwenhoek sent drawings of the 'vessels' and the 'little animals in the seed' to the Royal Society; these are the first of their kind in the literature. Leeuwenhoek wrote (March 18th, 1678) that he was 'glad to see that Viscount Brounker was exceedingly pleased to receive his letters.' In the same letter he replied to the Royal Society (who had asked him to institute observations on the sperm of dogs, horses and other animals): 'It would seem to be easy to observe the sperm of dogs, but . . . in my opinion it will have to be that of animals which eject their seed with force, such as horses, bulls, rabbits, etc. . . . I must use this seed at once without loss of time lest it should change into a watery matter. I hardly see my way to do this, as I require my customary seat and instruments, which I cannot place everywhere for use.' Grew, the Secretary of the Royal Society, also wrote to Leeuwenhoek that 'our Harvey and your Dr de Graaf' did not find sperm in the oviducts and so thought that the male sperm was 'nothing but the vehicle of a certain extremely volatile animal spirit, impressing on the conception (i.e. the ovum) the perception of life.' In reply Leeuwenhoek defended and further formulated his animalistic idea of fertilization. It has been said that Leeuwenhoek was a man of 'mediocre mind, but with marvellous hands and keen eyes. . . . Truly he was a pair of hands directed by other minds.' Surely, this is disproved by the fact that only a few years after the beginning of his researches we here find him in opposition to the great authorities, Harvey, de Graaf, and the members of the Royal Society.

'If I readily accept that your Harvey and our de Graaf never found any semen in a matrix cut up immediately after conception; for I state that as soon as the male's semen has entered the matrix, the female must supply the necessary nutrition for the preservation of the sperm. . . . For the entire matter in the eggs of hens, etc. (except what comes from the cock) I consider to have no other purpose than to serve as food for the semen. . . . If your Harvey and our de Graaf had seen the hundredth part they would have stated as I did that it is exclusively the male sperm that forms the foetus and that all the woman may contribute only serves to receive the semen and feed it.

'I intended to make no further observations on this subject

because I had sufficiently ascertained what I had communicated, but as you say that you have doubts about it because you do not see the purpose of nature in this respect, I intend to continue my observations. As for me, I fail to see why Nature should in vain make not only arteries, veins and sinews previously present in the semen, but even parts or at least germs of the heart, lungs and reproductive organs.' This is the old idea of Empedocles, which Leeuwenhoek later repudiated. He then examined the sperm of rabbits and found 'a number of living animalcules'; in the sperm of fishes he found at that date only 'globules.'

The structure of the ovary

In the ovaries (which he called 'testes') of cows and lambs he saw that the eggs were lying, 'each in a separate membrane, which is very strong. . . . These were on all sides connected with other parts, from which they could not be separated except by tearing their vessels and sinews in pieces.' These were the follicular membranes; Leeuwenhoek continues: 'Moreover, these eggs are enveloped in a second membrane encompassing the entire testicle'—obviously a reference to the germinal epithelium covering the ovary. 'In order to bring about the function described by Dr de Graaf, the so-called eggs would, in the course of the copulation, get separated from their strong parts . . . pierce the integument of the testicle and at the same time place the Fallopian tube with its aperture on the severed egg, to receive the latter. To me this seems to be altogether at variance with Nature, because we see how perfect Nature is in all these ways; a reason why I cannot agree with these views. But I leave this to others; only request you to be satisfied with what I saw.'

We must now admit that de Graaf was right in maintaining that the ovaries contain eggs, but he was mistaken in supposing that the follicles with their contents were the actual eggs. During ovulation, the follicle bursts open, and the actual egg-cell escapes through the opening and enters the Fallopian tube. Though de Graaf was the first to postulate such a sequence of events, he did not see the real egg, which was, in fact, discovered in 1827 by K. E. von Baer. In his letter of January 22nd, 1683, and again in 1716, Leeuwenhoek gave the arguments which made him reject de Graaf's opinions, pointing out that the Fallopian tube has 'the diameter of a pin,' whereas the 'eggs' (=follicles) were 'as great as peas.' Although in his letter of March 18th, 1678, he stressed his opinion that the 'vessels played a prominent part in the formation of the embryo,' in the next year (April 25th) he declared 'at one time I thought that the fibres or vessels came from the testicles, and that the animalcules were produced in the virile member' but 'I have found by dissection that the little animals were living in the testicle.' It is very remarkable that Leeuwenhoek, at that time, obviously had no objections to the views of Empedocles that there were loose organs in the semen; in 1677-78 he believed that there were organized parts of the embryo in the seminal fluid.

It seems likely that Leeuwenhoek, in common with the opinions of his time, was in agreement with Galen's theory of the spirits. It was thought that there were three different spirits—the natural spirit (*spiritus naturalis*) which gives unconscious life such as the plants possess, the vital spirit (*spiritus vitalis sive sensitivus*) which was formed in the heart and encompassed feeling and motion, and the animal spirit (*spiritus animalis*) situated in the brain and spread by the hollow tubes of the nerves; this latter spirit gives a conscious life. For Leeuwenhoek, life was synonymous with motion; he saw the spermatozoa swimming and moving while the egg lay quiet, and wrote (April 25th, 1679): 'Some imagine that these animalcules do not live, but that it is only the fire that is present in the sperm (i.e. the *innate heat* of Aristotle). But I take it that these animalcules are composed of such a multitude of parts as such people believe compose our bodies.' He continues: 'Although I am convinced that these observations . . . will be accepted by few people because it is impossible for so small a quantity of matter to contain so many living creatures, I will bear those who reject it no grudge, the less so because, when I wrote about the great number of living creatures in water, even the Royal Society would not accept it. For as truthfully as I wrote about the animalcules in water, so truthfully also do I write about the little animals in the male sperm of human beings, quadrupeds, birds and fishes; and I shall be satisfied if yourself (Nehemiah Grew) and the learned philosophers will only credit me, of which I have no doubt.' These are the words of a man who is sure of himself and who is not afraid of fighting for his beliefs. The 'vessels' he was to deny in later years, but the 'animalcules in the sperm' he discovered in all the species he examined and he was convinced of their reality.

Leeuwenhoek, naturally, computed the number of spermatozoa in the milt of a cod, and he arrived at the figure of '150,000,000,000 little animals in the milt of a cod, with a capacity of fifteen cubic inches.' As he thought that in his day there were 13,385,000,000 human beings on the earth, this meant that there were 'more than ten animalcules in the milt of one cod as against one human being on the earth's surface.' This posed the question: Where do the animalcules in the semen come from? It was certain that they must be formed very quickly, as the milt of fishes develops in a few days; nowadays we are accustomed to thinking of such problems in terms of the cell theory, but as this was not propounded until 1838, Leeuwenhoek had to find another solution.

The origin of the spermatozoa; Leeuwenhoek's preformistic ideas

In his letter of January 22nd, 1683, Leeuwenhoek declared that he saw the 'eggs' (follicles) which had burst open; he now continued: 'I unconditionally reject the strings lying   93 intertwined in sperm' and that 'I remember having seen that in the sperm of a man and also of a dog, there are two sorts of animalcules. Seeing these I imagine that one sort were males and the other females.' The Dutch histologist, Dr Heringa, thinks that Leeuwenhoek probably mistook additional matter or ill-formed spermatozoa for a second type of organism. Although this is the most probable explanation, it is interesting to note that at the present time it is known that there are two types of spermatozoa, differing in their chromosome content, which give rise to male and female offspring; these spermatozoa are, however, morphologically identical.

Leeuwenhoek wrote in March, 1685, that 'he had for some time firmly held that the animalcula in the male seed consist of two kinds'; in the Latin edition of his letters this is rendered even more emphatically as 'I was convinced beyond all doubt' (*extra aleam omnis dubitationis*). From the 'male spermatozoon' he thought that male offspring would be produced, and conversely. He now admitted that the seminal animalcule is not a small child, even though it produces a small child, any more than the seed of an apple is a tree, even though it gives rise to a tree. In his letter dated June 9th, 1699, he wrote: 'Now it is certain, that although we cannot discover the shape of a frog in an animal that is come from the egg of a frog when we anatomize it, yet the frog is locked up in it. . . . We know that the small animals in the male seed of a frog have no similitude at all with those that come out of the eggs of a frog.' Thus it is that the child in the animalcule does not resemble the child to be born. 'I put this down as a certain truth, that the shape of a human body is included in an animal of the male seed, but that a man's reason shall dive or penetrate into this mystery so far that in the anatomizing of one of these animalcules of the male seed, we should be able to see or to discover the entire shape of a human body, I cannot comprehend.' He then added: 'I have also observed, that between these animals lay some smaller roundish parts, and these have seemed to me, as if they had tails, wherefore I took into consideration whether these parts might not be young animals, for certainly these animals shall procreate . . . and who knows, whether these animals do not come to their perfect bigness in the space of twenty-four hours, as we have observed in small water-animals.' So Leeuwenhoek thought the animalcules were male and female and could procreate themselves in that shape. The quick growth of the milt was now explained, according to Leeuwenhoek!

Here we have the idea of preformation in a strongly marked form: the shape of a human body is included in a spermatozoon which can procreate itself, as such, because there are male and female animalcules. His concept does not include the idea that the form of the full-grown animal is identical with the form of that in the spermatozoon, and Leeuwenhoek thought it would, both in his time and in the future, be impossible to see the entire shape of the full-grown body in the sperm. However, others claimed to have seen the shape of a little human body in the spermatozoon; De la Plantade (1670–1741), writing under the name of Dalenpatius, declared that he had seen this. Leeuwenhoek disputed this observation as firmly as he could in his letter of June 9th, 1699, and in order to show how ridiculous was this opinion of Dalenpatius, he included in his own works two pictures taken from this author; this has led some historians of biology to conclude that Leeuwenhoek himself had seen such forms.

In 1694 Hartsoeker had given a similar figure, but as Cole (1930) pointed out, 'In referring to the homuncules which he figures, he says that *if* we could see the little animal through the skin which hides it we *might* possibly see it as it is represented in the illustration. . . . He therefore does not claim that the figure is based on anything more than supposition.'

The propagation of Volvox

Leeuwenhoek remained a preformationist and was strengthened in this opinion by the discovery of *Volvox*; it is therefore necessary at this point to digress a little and describe this discovery, and the researches which his views on reproduction led him to make in connection with the generation of plants.

On January 2nd, 1700, Leeuwenhoek wrote: 'I had the foresaid water taken out of the ditches and runnels on the 30th of August, 1698 . . . and I saw floating in it a great many green, round particles, of the bigness of sand-grains. . . . They were not simply round, but their outermost membrane was everywhere beset with many little projecting particles (=the individuals which compose the colony) . . . so that upon so small a body there stood a full two thousand of the said projecting particles. . . . This was for me a pleasant sight, because the little body . . . never lay still; and because too their progression was brought about by a rolling motion; and all the more because I imagined at first that they were animalcules. . . . Each of these little bodies had enclosed within it 5, 6, 7, nay, some even 12, very little round globules, in

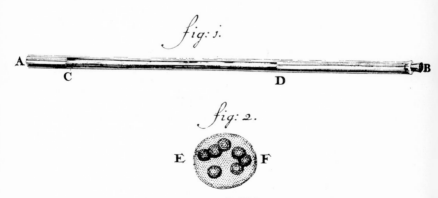

PLATE 8 *Volvox*

structure like to the body itself wherein they were contained'
(Plate 8).

'While I was keeping watch, for a good time, on one of
the biggest round bodies . . . I noticed that in the outermost
part an opening appeared, out of which one of the enclosed
globules, having a fine green colour, dropt, and took the
same motion in the water as the body out of which it came.
. . . Many people, seeing these bodies moving in the water,
might swear that they were little living animals. . . .' He put
two *Volvox* of the biggest type in a little glass tube, each
containing five little round particles, and a third with seven.
'After the space of five days I perceived that the small particles enclosed in the third large body were not only grown
in bigness, but I could also discern that from inside these
small particles, other smaller round particles were to come
forth.' Leeuwenhoek actually saw the daughter colonies within *Volvox* not yet themselves released from the parent! As
Dobell remarks: 'This acute observation gave great support
to the doctrine of the preformationists at a later epoch,
though it was then usually accredited to Spallanzani—who
in fact merely repeated and confirmed Leeuwenhoek's observations.' One interesting point which is of some importance
is that Leeuwenhoek did not mistake *Volvox* for an animal,
even though it could move so rapidly.

As Leeuwenhoek had a unitarian conception of nature, it
is not surprising that he thought that the process of propagation was the same in both animals and plants, and this led
him to pay much attention to the seeds of plants. It is
obviously impossible to review all his researches in this subject, but it is necessary to give a few examples in order to
show how this type of study influenced his opinion.

The propagation of plants

In his letter of July 13th, 1685, he writes: 'And if in the small
seeds of the ash there are to be seen not only perfect leaves   97

G

with their vessels, but the woody part also, and that part from which the root shoots out (nay plainer than in the walnut or hazel) we may well conclude that wise nature proceeds after the same manner in all its operations of generation or propagation; every seed containing not only the rudiments of the future plant, but also a certain fine flour to nourish it so long, till, striking root into the earth, it may thence receive its nutriment. This flour is of an oily nature, and the more oily the longer will the seeds remain out of the ground. And as plants are not *male* and *female*, nor have a matrix (=womb) for the first reception and sustenance of the young, so the parent tree produces a perfect plant wrapt up in the seed which the earth receives and nourishes. . . . I question whether the trees which we find may therefore be called *male* trees.' In the past, a species which was larger than another was often called male, whilst the lesser was the female; again with dioecious plants, sometimes the larger plant (usually in fact the female) was called the 'male.' Camerarius experimented with the problem of sex in plants in 1694, but Leeuwenhoek did not know of his work; study of the scientific literature was out of the question for as he stated in his letter of January 22nd, 1676, 'I must confess, to my sorrow, that I do not know any tongue but the Nether-Dutch, in which I was brought up.' It has been said that 'this bourgeois satisfait . . . took a pride in the fact that he knew neither French, Latin, English nor German,' but as Dobell has said, 'this is clearly contradicted by the words "to my sorrow" .' Although this lack of languages may be considered a weakness, it was an advantage to Leeuwenhoek, in that it led him to find the way for himself and not be influenced by the opinions of others. In this particular instance, however, it would have been an advantage for him to have had knowledge of the experiments of Camerarius.

Leeuwenhoek continues his letter with the following
words: 'I think it now past all doubt, that the Generation of

Animals is from an *animalcule* in the *male sperm*, and though I have often fancied that I have discovered the parts and membranes of the foetus in the animalcule . . . yet I will affirm nothing herein, till I shall be so lucky as to find an animalcule large enough to discover this truth, which I am not quite in despair of, since I have been so fortunate in the small seeds of the ash, to meet with leaves and rudiments of the future plant far larger than in the seed of any plant I have yet examined.

'If we compare plants with birds we shall find that as in birds which are male and female, it is necessary for the animalcule of the male already endowed with a living soul to be placed near the yolk of the egg of the female . . . so in plants the embryo is placed next to a sort of fine flour which I compare to the yolk of the egg. . . . Although I have formerly asserted, that the female served only to afford nourishment to the animalcules of the male sperm, and that plants grow out of the substance wherewith they are watered; yet I acknowledge for a certain truth, that a great variety is caused by the nourishment received from the mother. So by a horse and a she-ass, a mule is generated, which is like neither but participates of both . . . since the ass abounding in that nourishment which produced the ears and wanting that which gives a long tail, it must necessarily be like the mother in those two particulars. . . .

'And thus the plants receive a great alteration from the different soils in which the seeds are planted. . . . And I believe if we could take the embryo plant out of one seed and put it into another, so far as it would grow, we should have a new plant like to neither: as if we should take the embryo out of the walnut (which I will liken to the animalcule of the horse) and so join it to the seed of the chestnut (which I compare to the matrix of the ass) that it would grow, the plant produced by this union would be a new and unknown tree.' Naturally this experiment failed (especially as he did not recognize the cotyledons), but, as the quotation clearly shows, Leeuwenhoek tried to tackle the problem experimentally.

In his letter of August 24th, 1688, he describes the embryo of wheat and barley on successive days after the beginning of germination, noticing the 'ears' after about a month, and he succeeded in making a preparation of them. (Plate 28.)

The above quotation indicates Leeuwenhoek's views on the nature of hybrids, which can be seen still better in his letter of July 16th, 1683. 'It is my fixed opinion that if (in oviparous animals) no animalcule of the male sperm reaches the spot or dot in the egg (which, I think, is exclusively fit to receive the animalcule and to give it its first food in due time or to keep it in its original form from the moment it has been placed in the yolk till the egg is hatched) the egg will be sterile, and that for that reason there must be . . . so many thousands of animalcules for every single egg . . . in order that one animalcule out of many may hit the little dot or spot in the yolk. . . . I have several times tried to discover the animalcules of the male sperm of a cock in the yolk of the egg, but I have not succeeded in this until now. . . . I discontinued my attempts to find the male animalcule in the hen's egg and turned to an investigation of the male animalcule in the egg of a flea and of a louse, because, these eggs being very small, I might the more easily discern the animalcules, but in this I did not succeed either up till now. . . .

The rule of dominance

'Methinks, under correction, that it would suffice to give what follows as a proof enabling me to see that the foetus proceeds only from the male sperm and that the female only serves to feed and develop it. Many people here keep rabbits, some for pleasure, others for profit. Usually these rabbits are big and white and have long ears, which are accounted one of their beauties. In order to cause these white rabbits to have grey young, that they may sell these in spring for wild ones, they mate a grey buck with the white does. This grey buck (a fast grey they call it) which was caught when still young, in our dunes where all rabbits are grey, is mated not only with white, but also with piebald, blue and black does, and all the young issuing from this take their father's grey colour; and indeed it has never been seen that any such young rabbit had a single white hair or any other hair than grey. Moreover, they will never grow to the size of the mother, nor have long ears; also they will never be so tame as the mother, but will always remain rather wild.' Dobell pointed out (1915) that this is the first mention of a phenomenon which after Mendel's experiments (1865) became known as 'dominance.'

Not until 1875 did Oscar Hertwig succeed in tracing the course of a spermatozoon in a frog's egg; no wonder that Leeuwenhoek, who had not used any staining techniques, was unsuccessful, but at least he recognized the problem. That large numbers of spermatozoa are necessary in order to increase the chances of a spermatozoon of finding the germinal spot, is basically correct, as Leeuwenhoek realized; in other words, he compared it with what we call 'the struggle for existence.' In this same letter he wrote, 'I also think that, when the egg is being hatched, these animalcules will not instantly assume the form of the chicken, but will grow in what seems to us an irregular way: that is to say, that we believe that we can see the heart originate first of all.' He was certainly astonished at the fact that the embryo does not at once show the shape of the fully hatched animal, but the quotation proves that he did not believe that the future animal as such is in the animalcule. He knew 'that Man, even when the length does not exceed the diameter of a green pea, is already furnished with all his members.' Leeuwenhoek may have seen a few weeks' old embryo during a demonstration in the anatomical theatre, where the physicians and their assistants met every Wednesday, and such an embryo would provide a strong argument for the preformistic theory.

The duration of life of a spermatozoon

Leeuwenhoek tried to determine experimentally the duration of life of the animalcules in the semen. In his letter dated April 25th, 1679, he writes that he examined the testes of a cock. 'In the vasa deferentia I saw an enormous number of living animalcules such that I was quite amazed. . . . I followed this vas deferens up to the testicle and saw in it also a great number of little animals. But among them lay spread very many small globules, as also many flat, oval figures, whose circumference was about the size of a globule of blood (i.e. a red blood corpuscle). One would be inclined to attribute life to them on account of their movements, but I judge that all these were caused by the little animals, as was indeed the case. But I thought whether these flat oval particles could not well be animalcules which lay intertwined and had not yet received life: for if I cut up the largest of eels or snakes which are found in summer in vinegar, in order to take the young eels out of their bodies, these unborn eels lay twisted up in oval shapes.' (Leeuwenhoek described this viviparity of the vinegar eel, *Anguillula aceti*, for the first time quite correctly in his letter of October 9th, 1676; it was an important contribution to the knowledge of generation.) For Leeuwenhoek, as for others in his time, a *living* animalcule was a *moving* one, so he thought that the youngest stages 'had not yet received life.'

Regarding man he said, in his letter of April 5th, 1680, 'What shall we say about their origin? Shall we imagine that the seed of these animalcules is already existent, even during the moment of conception, and that this semen keeps lying in a man's testicles till he has attained the years of fourteen, fifteen, or sixteen years, and that the animalcules do not come to life or are full grown till at that time, and that then there is a possibility of generation? But I leave this question to others.' Now we will leave the origin of the animalcules, and describe his experiment on their duration of life.

In his letter of March 31st, 1685, he writes: 'About the latter end of the summer of the year 1683 I took the *semen masculinum* of a dog, which was about a year and a half old. This I put into a glass pipe and wrapt it up in soft leather, because the nights were something cold. This semen I observed four days successively, and in the first I found that several of its animals were dead. In the second and third day there were yet more of them dead, but on the fourth there were very few of them alive: and so far I proceeded at that time. But in the beginning of October in the year 1684, I observed again the *semen masculinum* of the same dog, who was then very strong and vigorous, and I found that after seven days and nights there were some few animals yet left alive, a very few whereof swam as briskly as if they had just come from the dog. From this I infer that these animals would have lived a much longer time if they had been in the *uterus*; also that conception in females is not always made *immediate post congressum*, but sometimes nine, or ten or more days after it, if one of the animals can find the *punctum* or the proper place for its nourishment; and lastly that the *uterus* may not be fit for the reception of animals at one time, though before two or three days are past it may become perfectly capable.

'I know my opinion on generation has been rejected by several persons, some of whom being skilled in anatomy have affirmed to me, that the semen masculinum never comes into the uterus, that it is never to be seen in that place and that it is nothing but a vapour which causes fruitfulness. . . . I remember that our Dr. de Graaf constantly asserts that the semen masculinum is nothing but a vehicle of a certain volatile salt, or such like spirit, conveying to the egg of the female a *contactum vitale*. But though a late writer has reckoned up the authorities of seventy persons who have asserted the same opinion, and that of the ovarium, yet I think they are all mistaken.'

He also wrote: 'I bespoke a bitch to be delivered to me after she had been once lined.' He killed her after she was lined again in his presence, and he opened the middle of the cornu . . . 'and I saw to my great satisfaction a very great many of the living animals of that semen. . . . Then I opened that part of the uterus which is between the vagina and the cornu . . . and here I found in the uterus a greater number of the living animals than before. After three and a half hours' time I went to communicate this my discovery to an eminent physician and anatomist . . . and I showed him the substance contained in the uterus (in another place), having a great number of living animals of the semen masculinum, though the weather was very cold and freezing. . . . The said physician remained convinced that generation was more clearly explained after my way than by eggs sucked out of the ovarium. . . .

'It is supposed that animals while they grow in the womb have a living soul; now if this be so, it is a thousand times more likely that the soul which is in the *Animalia seminis masculina* should still remain there, changing their outward shape, than that they should pass into another body' (i.e. the egg).

'Likewise I believe, that what is called frigidity in some men, is either a want (in them) of the *animalia seminis*, or a weakness in the animals which renders them unable to live long in the womb. I have often been considering, whether the opening of the Fallopian tube might not be to give way for the evacuating some moisture at the time the uterus is closed . . . for I have sometimes found in the thin part of the Fallopian tube near the opening, a white stuff consisting of transparent globules, a little bigger than a blood globule.'

This passage is characteristic of Leeuwenhoek; he attempted this problem in an experimental manner and was not dismayed by the authority of Harvey, de Graaf and 'seventy others.' Leeuwenhoek concluded from his experiments that copulation was not necessarily identical with conception, as the spermatozoa were capable of surviving for several days in the female genital tract. In the present age, when artificial insemination is well known, the techniques of storing spermatozoa, mixed with glycerol, and keeping them alive for many weeks at a temperature of $-79°C$ are familiar ones. It was Leeuwenhoek, however, who made the first experiments along these lines, though, very naturally, he thought that cold was a handicap to their survival. The identity of the 'transparent globules' in the Fallopian tube is not known with certainty—they may have been eggs. This explanation would not have suggested itself to Leeuwenhoek, as he believed, along with de Graaf and Swammerdam, that the 'follicles' in the ovary were the eggs, and these had a diameter many times that of a blood globule. As Leeuwenhoek found 'animalcules' in the sperm of thirty different animal types, it would be thought impossible for anyone to deny the existence of spermatozoa in normal semen. However, in 1749, Buffon declared that they were generated by putrefaction, and in 1814 the famous Johannes Müller wrote that he was not firmly convinced that they were a constituent of normal sperm, and that they might be parasites! Later, when the cell-theory was developed, these spermatozoa came to be thought of as body cells and it became evident that Leeuwenhoek had made a very important discovery by finding the 'animalcules' in the seminal fluid.

The ovulists, also, had basic facts to support their own theory, and Leeuwenhoek provided them with one of their best arguments; in his letter of October 26th, 1700, he described the 'Parthenogenesis' of the 'flies on trees.' He had already (in 1695) studied the plant lice or Aphids on fruit 105 trees and he had seen that they were viviparous (see Plate 15). He had looked at the species *Myzus ribes* and he said that he could not find any males. In 1700 he affirmed what he had already stated, 'that the Aphidae bring forth their young without coming together' or 'without the male kind.' Cole in his study of 1937 gives the following summary:

'This discovery had to be reconciled with his impeccable theory of generation. He was already deeply committed to the animalculist doctrine, and was evidently not prepared to consider the propriety of abandoning it. Believing, therefore, that the spermatic animalcule is a foetus, and is solely responsible for the embryo, how is generation possible in the absence of males? Leeuwenhoek's reply to this difficult question is boldly to rank the parthenogenetic Aphidae with the spermatozoa, which he *now* says do not arise from an act of copulation *inter se*. We therefore reach the curious impasse that an *Aphis* is a spermatic animalcule, and it is thus the *female* element that is wanting in these animals! . . . Leeuwenhoek opened some young *Aphis* and saw immature embryos in them. On dissecting other specimens he found the embryos proportionally advanced. . . . His final reference to the generation of Aphidae was in 1713, but in this letter he only remarks that all *Aphis* belong to the female sex and are viviparous.'

It is unfortunate that Leeuwenhoek was too saturated in animalculism to see that the fact of parthenogenesis which he himself had discovered was fatal to that doctrine, and his subtle but inglorious escape from the dilemma is a warning to those who are always ready to mould observation to speculation. What is still more surprising, however, is that the ovists should not have used this opening to declare to the world that here at last was a complete vindication of their creed. This was left to Charles Bonnet (1720–1793) who took this step after a careful study of the Aphids many years after the death of Leeuwenhoek. Abraham Trembley also contributed a careful study in 1740; he put forward the 'incapsulation' theory in which he refers not only to the Aphids and to *Volvox*, but also to *Hydra* and its budding.

Leeuwenhoek had also seen this phenomenon. In his letter of December 25th, 1702, he describes the asexual generation of *Hydra* (see Chapter Seven).

If we wish to gain some idea of the importance of Leeuwenhoek's researches into the problem of generation, we must think not only of the discovery of the spermatozoa in many species of animals, but also of the budding of *Hydra*, the conjugation and division of the Flagellates and Ciliates, the micro-dissections of plant seeds and young plants and the formation of the daughter colonies in *Volvox*. We must also remember his descriptions of the life cycles of so many animals and of his experimental studies on the duration of life of the spermatozoa. His contributions to the understanding of the subject were very remarkable and outstanding; though he made mistakes, they were few and mainly errors of interpretation rather than of observation.

CHAPTER FIVE

The Minute Structure of Tissues: Leeuwenhoek as a Histologist

In this chapter we shall give an account of some of Leeuwenhoek's fundamental discoveries in histology. As usual, his observations and conclusions in his first letters often differ from those in his later ones; sometimes in one letter he discussed many very different subjects, and he often returned during the course of his forty to fifty years of observation to some earlier topic and, if necessary, modified his conclusions. For convenience, Leeuwenhoek's remarks on various subjects will be collected and presented in his own words so that the development of his ideas can be followed more easily; like all scientists, Leeuwenhoek made assumptions at all stages of his research, and at first he adhered to a general 'globular theory' which later he came to reject.

The discovery of the red blood corpuscles and the capillaries

For many centuries man had known that blood was a very unusual fluid. Galen thought that blood from the left chamber of the heart and the arteries was the carrier of 'vital spirits,' whereas blood from the right ventricle and from the veins carried the 'natural spirits'; the hollow nerves were the containers for the 'animal spirits.' Harvey, in his famous book *On the Movement of the Heart and Blood* (1628), which was based entirely on observation and experiment, rejected the theory that the blood oscillates back and forth in the arteries and veins (the flux and reflux of Galen) and proposed that there was a circulation of the blood. This circulation was a double one, the Pulmonary or Lesser circulation beginning in the right side of the heart and going through the lungs to the left side, whilst the Greater or Systemic circulation passed from the left side to the right through the rest of the body. This theory gained acceptance in a few decades, though Harvey denied the existence of the thoracic duct (discovered by Aselli in 1622 and described in 1627) and he rejected the 'anastomoses' between the arteries and the veins. He wrote to Slegel (1651): 'I confess, I say, nay, I even pointedly assert, that I have never found any visible anastomoses. . . . Even in a dead animal it falls of its own accord through the finest pores of the flesh and skin from superior into inferior parts.' It is remarkable how some opinions of the great authorities may retard the progress of science and good observations may be neglected as they do not fit into any of the currently accepted theories. Two observations, one by Malpighi, the other by Swammerdam, were published on the subject of the blood, but as they were in Latin Leeuwenhoek was unaware of them. Malpighi wrote, in 1661, to Borelli that he had seen the blood circulating in the lungs of a frog, not in spaces, but in tubes; later, in 1665, he saw the red blood corpuscles but mistook them for globules of fat. Swammerdam also wrote on the red blood cells, and the capillaries, but this part of his work was not published until 1737 in the *Biblia Naturae*, so that obviously this work could not have influenced Leeuwenhoek.

In his third letter to the Royal Society (April 7th, 1674) Leeuwenhoek wrote: 'I cannot neglect this opportunity to tell you that I have endeavoured to see and know, what parts the blood consists of; and at length I have observed, taking some blood out of my own hand, that it consists of small round globules driven through a crystalline humidity of water; yet, whether all blood be such, I doubt.' He correctly observed that the blood when exposed to air is a brighter red near the surface; he did not ascribe this change in the superficial layer to the action of the air (i.e. a chemical action) but to the penetration of light (i.e. a physical effect). In his letter of June 1st, 1674, he described his manner of examining the blood, so that we know that he pricked himself with a needle, applied a slender glass pipe to the spot, let the blood run up it a little way and then smeared it on the pin of his microscope.

He thought that the red blood corpuscles were globules and throughout his life he adhered to the opinion that in mammals they were spherical. In later years he saw that they were flat, but he considered this to be because they had changed their form as they were so 'tender.' Leeuwenhoek also abandoned the use of the glass capillary tube, spreading the blood in thin layers on a little plate of glass; moreover, he always examined the red cells in water, which causes an alteration in their form. After he had seen little pointed rods in the blood of the eel (which he thought caused the pain suffered after getting some of the blood in one's eye, October 5th, 1677), he saw in his own blood 'that the globules took the same figure which I formerly mentioned that the globules of the blood of eels appeared to the eye.' He thought that 'they were more pliable than I did imagine before, for they were three times as long as broad.' He thought that this flattened shape was due to deformation and that when they came into a larger space they would recover their former globular shape.

In his letter dated June 1st, 1674, Leeuwenhoek not only described the globules but also measured them: 'The red globules of the blood I reckon to be 25,000 times smaller than a fine grain of sand.' In his letter of May 20th, 1679, he gives 1/80 inch as the diameter of such a grain; in his letter of March 3rd, 1682, however, he quotes 1/100 inch, which is about 260μ. Assuming that in such a grain of sand 25,000 blood corpuscles can be contained, their diameter appears to be 1/30th of the diameter of a sand grain, i.e. approximately 8·5μ, which agrees closely with the modern measurement of 7·2μ, or 1/3,200 inch. In 1723, J. Jurin wrote that the diameter was 1/1,940 of an inch (13μ approximately) but Leeuwenhoek, who died in August of that year, did not believe this to be true (letter, March 19th, 1723).

As usual, Leeuwenhoek was not satisfied with the examination of his own blood, but extended his observations to various animals. In his letter of March 3rd, 1682, he says: 'Observing this blood (of a ray) it struck me that the parts of the blood that are globules in human beings and mammals, and colour the blood red, are here all of them flat, oval particles, thickish, floating in a crystalline water. Where these oval particles lay single, they had no colour, but when three or four lay on top of each other they began to show colour. Thus I came to observe the blood of a cod and of a salmon, which I also found to consist of hardly anything but oval figures, and however closely I tried to observe these, I could not make out of what parts these oval particles consisted, for it seemed to me that some of them enclosed in a small space a little round body or globule.' This is the first observation of the *nucleus*! He not only described it, but also gave a good picture (Plate 9), the first in the literature. In other blood-cells he saw 'three, four, five, six—nay, as many as eight globules,' a phenomenon which can easily be observed in salmon's blood heated to a temperature of about 40°C, when vacuoles are formed in the cells.

The origin of the blood cells

The burning question in Leeuwenhoek's time was, 'Where and how was the blood made?' Galen thought that the blood vessels coming from the intestines (vena porta) carried particles from the food. The liver made the blood from these particles, it being the seat of the 'calor innatus' and of the 'natural spirits.' (In the intestines there were 'ostia' or little openings giving entrance to the blood vessels.) The discovery

fig 4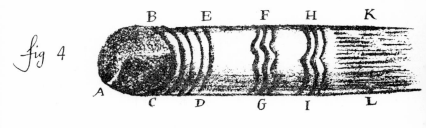

fig: 5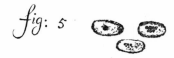

PLATE 9 *Muscle fibres and red blood cell of a fish with nucleus*

of the lacteals and thoracic duct showed that the liver could not be the site of blood formation and so the question was again open. Leeuwenhoek had to form his own opinion of the way in which the red cells of the blood were formed; in his letter dated January 14th, 1678, he describes the 'thorn-apple' appearance: 'To my great satisfaction, I finally saw very clearly that the blood-globules (in my own blood) internally consisted of globules enclosed in a tough vesicle; and withal, I took much pains to observe, the number of the same very small globules . . . at last I strongly imagined, that every one of the greater globules consisted of six smaller globules.' He thought that each of the little globules consisted in their turn of six smaller globules, and these again of six; so a red blood corpuscle should consist of $6 \times 6 \times 6 = 216$ little globules (Plate 10).

112

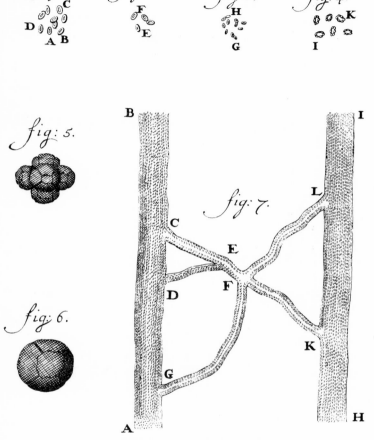

PLATE 10 *Red blood cells of fishes, capillaries and
model of a human red blood cell*

Leeuwenhoek denied the existence of ostia in the intestines but believed that a little particle of food with a diameter
of about 1μ (later, he said 0.001μ!) could pass through the
wall of the intestines and then coagulate with other particles
to form a blood cell. The quick movement of the blood would

113

H

give these coagulations their spherical form; he demonstrated this by forming a ball of clay from six little balls by rolling them in his hands. When he discovered the yeast cells, he thought that they were formed in the same manner (letter dated June 14th, 1680).

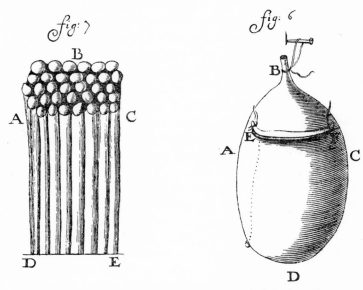

PLATE 11 *Ox-bladder experiment and villi of the intestines*

The structure of the intestines

Leeuwenhoek's discovery of the 'thready substance otherwise called the slime or woolly substance' (the villi of the intestines) (Plate 11) strengthened his opinions on the way in which food particles 'coagulated' to form blood cells. He performed an experiment by filling an ox-bladder with air, and a piece of gut with air and water, and hanging them in his chimney. After sixteen hours, all the water in the gut had run out, but none of the air was lost; 'nay, the gut seemed as stiff as when it was first blown' (Plate 11). He was thus

114

convinced that water could pass through the wall of the intestines, but air could not.

The discovery of the capillaries

We cannot discuss all Leeuwenhoek's observations on blood-cells (he discovered the white blood-cells in a shrimp, January 12th, 1683), but we shall draw attention to his discovery of the capillaries. In 1682, Leeuwenhoek found, in a cockroach, a connection between the 'vessels'; these were, however, not blood vessels, but air-tubes or *tracheae*. In the following year, he discovered the capillaries in the wall of the intestine: 'These blood vessels do not spread their branches on all sides, like the blood vessels in other parts of the body, but they lie in a bow, sending all their branches inwards, and none outwards. They lie so close by one another, that I imagine ten thousand of them may be in the space of an inch square. . . . The thickness or diameter is about the twenty-fifth part of a hair from my head. . . . From the foregoing observation, I have been doubtful whether the arteries and veins were not in this place joined together . . . for among all the experience that I have had of the blood vessels I never perceived such a probability of the Anastomosis. . . . These observations make me more than ever reject the opinion that the extremities of the lacteal and lymphatic vessels have mouths or openings, whereby they receive and take in the chyle out of the guts.'

In his letter dated September 7th, 1688, he gives his classic description of the circulation of the blood in the gills of a tadpole. 'These parts (the external gills) alone caused me to have the tadpole drawn: for in each of these parts I saw to my great amusement very clearly the circulation of the blood, which was pushed along from the parts nearest to the body to those farthest away from it, thus performing a continuous very swift circulation. The blood did not circulate smoothly, for in a very short time it was again driven along, and continually so; and before this very quick impulse took place, we should have thought that a standstill in the circulation would have followed if we had not seen a continual progress in the course of the blood. But hardly had a movement of the blood slowed down, when another very quick impulse followed: hence a continuous circulation took place in the blood of this animal. And if I try accurately to measure the short time between each of these impulses, I must say that in the time a rapid tongue could hardly count up to a hundred, there were as many as a hundred quick impulses of the blood. From this I concluded that an equal number of times the blood was driven from the heart. And so distinctly was this movement of the blood being driven from the heart and the transition of the arteries into the veins, as neither myself nor anyone else could imagine.'

Leeuwenhoek now looked at the heart and he saw it move just as often as the blood was driven out. (He did not shrink from vivisection in order to test his opinions experimentally.) He followed the circulation from the aorta to the inferior vena cava: 'This proved to me that the blood vessels we see in this animal and which we call arteries and veins are one and the same blood vessels; they can be called arteries only so long as they carry the blood to the farthest parts of the small blood vessels, and veins when they carry the blood to the heart again.' Following up this work, he examined the different forms of the blood corpuscles and saw that several 'globules' were extended to twice their breadth and gave the impression of being pointed at both ends.

Leeuwenhoek went on to say, 'Though we have now had the great fortune (to which we have been looking forward and which we have ever been seeking in vain) to show clearly the circulation of the blood and its passing from the arteries into the veins in the above-mentioned frog and fishes, yet we shall not rest, but do our duty also to examine other animals and, if possible, detect the same things in them.'

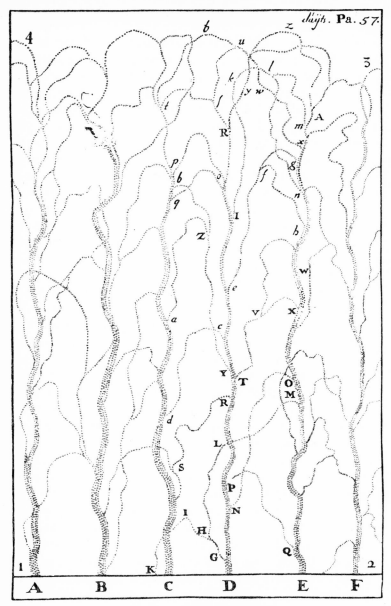

PLATE 12 *Blood capillaries*

Since he was so often contradicted, he took the precaution to mention at once some witnesses who also saw the circulation of the blood. He did not mention whether any one of them had drawn his attention to the description of the circulation which Malpighi had given, so we may assume that Malpighi's remark had made no impression on him. Since Swammerdam's description had not yet been published, Leewenhoek could consider himself the man who had solved the problem of the connection between arteries and veins. He could not tear himself away from this problem and his next letter was again entirely devoted to it. Having constructed his complicated 'aalkijker' or 'apparatus' for observing the circulation in the tail of an eel, he asserted, 'that the smallest blood vessel has a wall, consisting of three separate membranes, just as the arteries and veins, yet, this being the case, the walls of these tiny blood vessels must be most thin. . . . Summing up, we come to the following conclusion: though each of the smallest blood vessels is provided with a wall, this said wall is so thin, open or spongy, that the thinned watery liquid in the blood can get through it easily as water through a sieve.' This was an important step forward, in which Leeuwenhoek took the modern point of view.

Leeuwenhoek was a man who was inclined to draw practical conclusions from his investigations. He was convinced that in illness the blood was too thick to go through the capillaries and he tried to 'dilute' it by drinking large quantities of tea and coffee! He traced experimentally the influence of different chemicals on the blood, of the poison of a spider on the blood of the frog, and of the poison of a scorpion on the blood of a lizard, but the above-mentioned discoveries of the blood-cells and capillaries are enough to convince us that in this field, too, Leeuwenhoek made very important contributions to our knowledge.

Leeuwenhoek's observations on the structure of nerves

The opinion of Galen, that the 'hollow nerves' carried the
'animal spirits' through the body, was widely held in Leeuwenhoek's time; thus, in a treatise published in 1655–66,
the English physician Thomas Willis declared that the optic
nerves were the conductors of 'spiritus animalis' and ended
in the outer wall of the eye. Leeuwenhoek wrote to Oldenburg (December 4th, 1674): 'You will oblige me by com-
municating what I am going to say hereafter about the visual
nerve to the famous and excellent anatomist Thomas Willis,
whose opinion I am anxious to hear.

'I took eight different optic nerves, and observed that after
those nerves had been but a little while cut off from the eye,
the filaments of which they are made up, did shrink up,
which shrinking up cannot be so much on the external
surface or coat of the nerve as it is of the filaments that lie
within the same: and upon this shrinking up, a little pit
comes to appear about the middle of the nerve; and it is this
pit in all probability that Galen took for a cavity. This I
remarked on all occasions. . . . Having dried such a nerve,
and made a transverse segment thereof, I not only saw in it
a hole, but very many, which made it resemble a leathern
sieve. . . . I am of the same opinion still that the nerves or
fibres are made up of soft fluid globules, and that these
globules by drying the nerve are most of them exhaled.' At
the time of this letter, Leeuwenhoek was of the opinion that
all, or nearly all, organic and inorganic matter consisted of
'globules,' an idea which he later rejected. Although it is not
possible to detail all Leeuwenhoek's observations on nerves,
his last letter (May 26th, 1717) on this subject is worth
mentioning. Cole summarizes this as follows:

'The nerves, he now says, are beyond question composed
of exceedingly small vessels or tubes running parallel with
each other—the cavity of the vessels being two-thirds the

diameter. Small as these cavities are, he says, he has seen aquatic animalculae so minute that they could have swum about in them with freedom. In fact the minuteness of some transcends all belief. He admits that in transverse section the

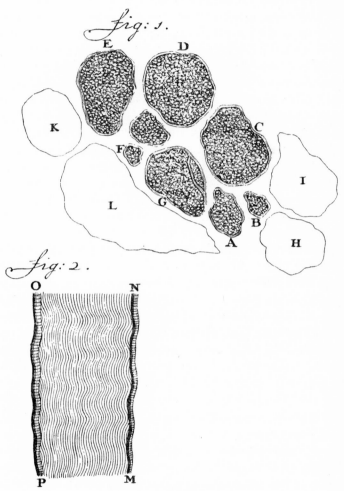

PLATE 13 *Nerve fibres*

nerve fibres may not seem to be tubular, since owing to the compression of the fibres the cavities are sometimes pressed flat, and then appear as a *line* in each tube.' This condition is illustrated in the figure (Plate 13) which shows a section of a nerve, with fat between the bundles of nerve fibres.

'Leeuwenhoek also found tubular nerve fibres in longitudinal and transverse sections of the spinal cord, and he claims that the light of the sun can be seen through the cavities of the fibres which had been cut across. He noted that the nerve fibres after leaving the cord *increased in size and were covered with a new membrane.* He holds that the nerve-tubes transmit a fluid humour which can evaporate, and in this humour the nerve force resides. This was a current belief, due largely to Descartes—a belief which survived until the middle of the last century. In the last two letters of his eighty-fourth year, he finds . . . that the nerve fibres were not all of the same size. Even when the nerves are so slender that they are no thicker than a hair of his beard, they are still made up of vessels like the larger nerves. He points out that a nerve consists of little bundles of fibres (funiculi) and that these bundles are collected together by membranes . . . which are independent and do not coalesce among themselves. . . . He compares the medullary sheath of the nerve fibre with the sarcolemma of the muscle.' It is clear from this that Leeuwenhoek, forty years after his first description of the optic nerve, saw the axons of nerve fibres and their myelin sheaths.

Leeuwenhoek's observations on muscles

In mediaeval times, the muscles were considered to be an 'instrument of the free will'; Caspar Bartholinus (1642) said they consisted of 'flesh, tendon, veins which bring back the food, arteries which bring the food and maintain the innate heat, nerves which transport the feeling and the movement, "membranes," and lastly the moistening fat, which prevents 121 the muscles to shrivel by great movements.' As this book was translated into Dutch in 1658, we may assume that Leeuwenhoek had read it. In 1664 and 1667 Steno published his studies on the muscles, in which he stated that the muscle is made up of 'fibres' (corresponding to what we now call fasciculi), each composed of 'very little fibres' (the muscle-fibres). Leeuwenhoek could not read these books, nor the famous work of Borelli *De motu animalium* (1680, 'On the motion of animals'). In this book Borelli was mainly concerned with the mechanistic problems of muscular movements and he did not investigate the histology of muscles. Swammerdam also studied muscles, probably in 1667, when he made the famous experiment which showed that the volume of a muscle did not alter on contraction; this led him to the conclusion that there were 'no animal spirits blown into it by the nerves,' a view which he did not publish until 1737, in the *Biblia Naturae*.

The first letter in which Leeuwenhoek refers to the histology of muscle is dated June 1st, 1674: 'Having divers times observed the flesh of a cow, I found it to consist of very slender filaments, lying one by the other as if woven into a film. I have also viewed several filaments, which were beset with globules. These globules I judge to be blood, and that, pricking our body with a pin without hitting a vein, the bloody globules did issue from between these filaments: but this I leave to others for consideration. Meantime, I have with a needle's point severed these filaments from one another and found the single one so fine, that any of them seemed to me some twenty-five times thinner and finer than a hair. Having exposed them to my microscope, I saw to my wonder that they were made up of very small conjoined globules, which in smallness surpass all the rest. This I took notice of frequently in various filaments, being unwilling to take up anything for truth but what I had seen divers times, 122 and in divers parts.'

As the muscle-fibres that comprise a muscle are about as thick as a hair, it follows that Leeuwenhoek must have teased these apart and separated some of the component myofibrils. At the time of these investigations he had not yet discovered the capillaries (see p. 115).

In 1677 (May 14th) he again saw the 'globules' but in 1682 he writes on March 3rd: 'I have in the past often said, that if I found that I was mistaken in my opinion I would publicly confess my error. The case is that I often imagined that I could distinctly see that the fleshy fibres (=the muscle-fibres) of which the greater part of a muscle consists, were made of globules, and it appeared to me that this was distinctly visible when I observed the flesh-fibres through an ordinary microscope after I had cut them across and pulled them asunder crosswise with a fine needle. . . . Once more I have taken the flesh of oxen and cows on several days. I concluded that the flesh-fibres are so thin that if fifty of them are put side by side they cover 1/22 of an inch.' (The muscle-fibres of a muscle vary in thickness from 10–40μ; Leeuwenhoek computes this value to be 25μ, which agrees well with the dimensions of what is now called a muscle-fibre.) 'This will come to 1,000 flesh-fibres for the length of one inch, that is to say 1,000,000 flesh-fibres enveloped in their membranes in one square inch. . . . My only purpose in inserting in this place my calculations of the flesh-fibres was to bring out their minuteness; the more so because a certain physician in our country* tries to state as a fact that these flesh-fibres are implanted in the mouth of the veins, and that they end in the arteries; also that the circulation of the blood passes through these fibres; nay, he maintains that he has seen that there are valves in them, and that he made these observations not by means of a microscope but with the naked eye, evidently having taken an entire minute muscle for a fibre.

* This was Stephen Blankaart, a most famous man; as usual Leeuwenhoek does not mention the name of a man with whom he disagrees.

'[Plate 9, fig. 4] is a flesh-fibre in which frequently the rings and wrinkles become apparent to me, and so (as I have said before) they looked like globules when seen through an ordinary microscope. Also a flesh-fibre showed the internal filaments which constitute a flesh-fibre. Since I observed this, I have been able to make out why our fingers, arms and legs, nay, our entire body cannot lie out stretched straight, when reposing, but must lie slightly bent, resembling the form we had when still in the womb. . . . I split a flesh-fibre that I might the more distinctly see the numerous filaments of which such a flesh-fibre consists. . . . From this I concluded that a flesh-fibre, which, as I have said before, is not thicker than 1/9th of a hair of my beard, consisted of as many as a hundred filaments. Nay, I have often imagined that I could see the filaments or vessels of the membranes of a flesh-fibre, in which the filaments lay enclosed or by which they were surrounded.'

In all probability the 'vessels of the surrounding membranes' were the connective tissue-fibres of what is now termed the endomysium. Although Leeuwenhoek discovered the striations of voluntary muscle, and saw the 'multangular or Cohnheim's areas,' he did not see that the fibrils inside the muscle-fibre are also themselves striated. As usual, Leeuwenhoek measured the structures which he was the first to see.

He naturally extended his observations to the muscles of other organisms, and he found the same type of structure; in April of 1694 he saw that the muscle-fibres of the hearts of birds, mammals and fish seem to anastomose. In his later years he devoted much of his time to the study of muscles and tendons. He thought that as an animal grew, the fibres of its muscles would become larger and thicker, so he compared the fibres of a perch weighing nine ounces with those of a perch of only one ounce. They were indeed twice as great, but when he examined the muscle of a whale, he found that the fibres were eight times smaller than those of a great cod. Notwithstanding this, he thought that there would be very small muscle-fibres in the cilia of the Protozoa.

Leeuwenhoek had seen the spirally wound stalk of *Vorticella* (see Chapter Three), the tracheae of insects, the tracheids in plants, and so he was glad to see (March 26th, 1715), that the wrinkles and shrinkings in the tendons and muscles were 'rotating or spiral parts' so strengthening his unitarian conception of nature. It is interesting to note that in our own day, the spiral concept of the structure of muscle has been revived (e.g. by Tiegs) but with little support.

Leeuwenhoek's observations on the eye

In the earlier part of this chapter, Leeuwenhoek's observations on the optic nerve have been mentioned, and as his discoveries on the compound eye of insects will be reviewed in Chapter Six, only his studies on the vertebrate eye will be considered here. One of his earliest observations on this subject can be found in his letter of September 7th, 1674; as usual, in those days he found that in nearly all the parts of the eye there were 'globules.' In the lens (the 'crystalline liquor') these were 'neatly arranged side by side and one above the other, that the light may pass through it straight.' In a subsequent letter (December 4th, 1674) he wrote: 'As one person has blue eyes and another brown ones, so I also speak of the brown colour which I saw in the ox's eye, and which I have found to consist of dark grey globules. I fancy that the blue we see in eyes consists of transparent and brown globules mixed together.' The Dutch histologist Professor Dr. Heringa remarked: 'The brown globules of the iris correspond with pigment cells. If one further assumes that the "transparent globules" are colourless fibrous matter, then Leeuwenhoek's explanation of the blue colour is perfectly correct, for if there is only little pigment, the iris is blue.'

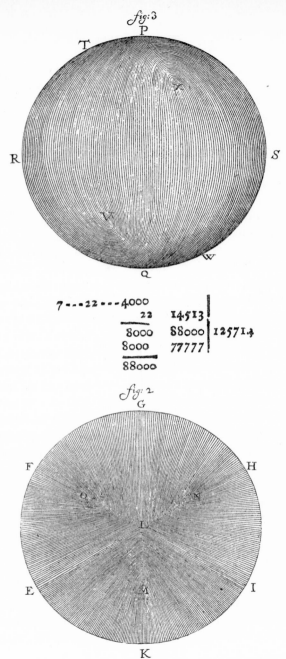

PLATE 14 *Lens of the eye. 2, front view; 3, side view; with the many thousands of fibres*

The structure of the lens

The most important discovery in this field is found in the letter of April 14th, 1684. 'For some time I have again made several observations concerning the eyes of oxen and cows, because I had often reflected (since my first observation) that I had not yet seen the exact structure of the crystalline body, as I ought to see it.' (Plate 14.) 'So I first examined the film or membrane (=capsula lentis) enclosing the crystalline body . . . and at one time I felt convinced that this film or membrane consisted of fibres, but at another time I could not discern any fibres in spite of my close observations. In the course of this research I rarely saw, however, that there were impressions of the fibrous substance of the outermost scale of the crystalline body on the before-mentioned membrane. . . . I further observed that this crystalline body consists of such thin layers, lying on top of each other, that measuring them by the eye, I cannot but say that two thousand lay on top of each other. For, after I had separated the crystalline body from its membrane, its axis in its thickest parts . . . still remained a thickness of 2/3rd of an inch. Its thickness from the centre to the circumference is therefore 1/3rd of an inch, and as according to my measurements six hundred breadths of a hair make one inch, the length of 1/3rd of an inch will be two hundred hairbreadths. Now I notice that when ten scales lie on top of each other they will not equal the diameter of a hair from my head. . . . I further observed that each of these scales consists of fibres (=the lens fibres) lying side by side in a very neat arrangement, so that each scale is one fibre thick.' He then gave a description of the structure of these scales. Professor Dr. Zeeman, the Dutch ophthalmologist, comments on this, 'Leeuwenhoek's analysis of the structure of the lens is amazingly accurate, despite some inevitable sketchiness in the picture he presents. He discovered that the lens consists of lens fibres, arrayed

in rows and forming films (Leeuwenhoek's small scales). . . .
The "scales" consist of stratified lens fibres lying alongside
each other forming a unit of 6–10μ wide and 3–4μ in thickness.' Leeuwenhoek calculated the number of the lens fibres
to be about 12,571.

Dr. Zeeman adds: 'Leeuwenhoek provided us with such a
sound knowledge of the lens capsule and the lens of the eyes
of many animals that the work of subsequent investigators—
done centuries later, and with the most modern methods of
investigation—has not been able to add much of importance
to this knowledge. . . . He observes in his description of the
lens of the ox that the fibres do not pass through the axis as
he thought at first, but from the point L (see fig. 14) which
is the imaginary axis, and then turn into three different paths
which do not end in the same axis on the other side of the
lens. Though Leeuwenhoek does not draw the lens sutures,
he does draw and describe precisely that peculiar course of
the lens fibres between the anterior and posterior Y-figures
which we now know from the work of later investigators. In
his figure one can easily draw the Y-figure which is formed by
the interior sutures, if we join the points marked O-N-M-L.
If he had not considered these fibres to be endless but to
be the short threads which he speaks of in several places,
then he probably would have drawn more clearly the points
of beginning and ending of these threads (i.e. the actual lens
sutures).'

Leeuwenhoek wrote in the same letter: 'I take a clean
wine-glass, the outermost rim of which I hold close to my
eyeball while shutting the other eye; then I look intently
through the brim of the glass at the flame of a burning candle
or any other luminous object, and in that manner the rim of
the glass shows such a fibrous substance as if we saw through
a microscope a piece of a scale taken from the crystalline
body of an animal. Or else, I keep one eye closed and hold
before the other the fingers of my hand so close together that

I only leave a narrow fissure between my fingers, through which the light of the candle will strike my eye; this will also show a fibrous character like that of the rim of the glass mentioned above.' Of this, Dr. Zeeman remarks: 'Leeuwenhoek is here describing the "entoptic spectrum of the lens".' Before Leeuwenhoek wrote to the Royal Society he studied the optic lenses of hares, rabbits, fishes and birds; besides being a true 'comparative anatomist' he was also greatly interested in the functions of the parts he described.

The structure of bone, teeth and hairs
TEETH

In 1678, Leeuwenhoek wrote: 'In my letters of 24th April, 1674 and 1st June, 1674, I wrote to tell you that bone consists of transparent globules. I also demonstrated this to several gentlemen who all attested this and had a high opinion of a magnifying glass through which things were seen so sharply. I adhered to this opinion till the first of May, when I drew with so great a force the back-tooth in my upper jaw which gave me great pain, and examined it closely in order to discover, if possible, the cause of its decay. During this examination I found that we erred with regard to the globules, which we imagined to see so distinctly that we could not but take them for globules; especially when I used much stronger glasses, with greater magnification, for then I could see quite clearly and distinctly that the whole tooth was made up of very small transparent pipes. Six or seven hundred of these pipes together, I judge do not exceed the thickness of one hair of a man's beard. In the teeth of a cow, the same pipes appear somewhat bigger, and in those of a haddock or cod, somewhat less.' Here one gains the impression that Leeuwenhoek, as a result of conscientious observation, gradually came to doubt his 'theory of globules'; again in his letter of March 3rd, 1682, he confessed his error concerning the structure of the muscle-fibres. Neither here,

129

I

nor in the letter of April, 1674, was Leeuwenhoek aware of the difference between dentine and bone. Nor did he as yet see any difference between dentine and enamel, but in his figures he clearly showed the structure of enamel as an acellular structure, consisting of prisms of calcium phosphate 4μ long set side by side. It is also worth noting that Leeuwenhoek also depicts these prisms as having a cross striation. The 'pipes' which he described in his letter were clearly the tubules found in dentine; here again we find that Leeuwenhoek studied the teeth of several species, so becoming, in fact, a comparative histologist.

Leeuwenhoek tried to measure the structures that he found in the teeth; in 1687, he thought that he saw 5,400 pipes in an inch. The tubules in the dentine are about $1-2\cdot5\mu$ in diameter and are separated from each other by 10μ; as Leeuwenhoek's value works out at about $4\cdot5\mu$ it is not clear whether he measured the cavities, or only their distance apart. It has already been said that Leeuwenhoek studied the bacteria of the teeth, so now it only remains to add a few words about his theory of the cause of toothache. Sir Hans Sloane sent him 'three small maggots, two of which were dead, with a letter informing me that they were found in a person's decayed tooth'. . . . 'On examining these, I had no doubt that they were of the sort found in cheese, and upon comparing them with some living ones which I procured from a cheesemonger, I found them to correspond exactly in make and shape.' He then tells the following amusing story (July 27th, 1700): 'I remember how for some years my wife, of blessed memory, was troubled with a very bad toothache and complained that something was going on inside her teeth, as if the flesh was being gnawed through. A doctor, of whom she was an aunt, was called more than once, but whatever treatment he applied, the pain remained. At last he agreed to our putting a drop of oil of vitriol in the hollow tooth. 130 To this end I contrived a glass instrument with which we could put a drop of vitriol in the hole of the tooth without injuring the gums, thinking in this way to kill the nerves that caused the pain. This was done, and shortly after the pain was gone. Now it may have been that she had one or more maggots in her hollow tooth. For she was eating with great zest some Edam cheese which was so old that it had started to decay; but as long as the decayed parts were whitish, this did not prevent her from eating it, though it contained many maggots. This being the case, these maggots to which we never gave a thought, might have caused the pain and been killed by the oil of vitriol.' Presumably no modern dentist would agree with this explanation, but this was probably one of the first nerve treatments.

THE STRUCTURE OF BONE

At first, Leeuwenhoek did not distinguish bone from dentine, but in his letter of May 31st, 1678, he wrote: 'I have also observed part of the shin bone of a calf, six or seven weeks old, in which the said pipes are less straight than in a tooth. And here sometimes there seemed to be several lesser pipes joined together, so as to constitute one greater. Yet these pipes were full of fat, which hindered my better observation of them. I am apt to think, that there was one sort of pipes different from the former, which are continued from the centre of the bone, towards the circumference, as the medullary rays do in the wood of a plant. But I doubt whether I shall be able hereafter more distinctly to discover these last-mentioned pipes, because I cannot handle the bone after my own pleasure.' Here Leeuwenhoek was evidently referring to the Haversian canals which ramify in the substance of the bone. In a later communication (April 2nd, 1686) Leeuwenhoek gave a description and a drawing (magnification about 130 times) of the structure of bone; here he clearly saw four sorts of tubes, the smallest of which were evidently the lacunae of the osteocytes. 131

HAIRS

In Hooke's *Micrographia* of 1665, there is a description of the structure of a hair, but two problems remained; one was whether there was a cavity or a medulla of soft cells in the centre of the shaft of the hair. The second problem was whether the growth of a hair was at the top, like that of a plant, or at the base in the skin. Leeuwenhoek easily solved this latter problem by the simple experiment of shaving himself and observing the pieces of hair. 'I got two pieces of hair from my face after shaving (three days in winter after my previous shave) which show the oblique edge that the knife usually makes, and that these are not at all like sprouts, which ought to be present if the hair did not grow by a process of pushing (from the base in the skin).' With regard to the cavity in the medulla, Leeuwenhoek thought that there were in the interior of the hair 'soft globules' which would shrink and retract to give the impression of a cavity. As with many other objects, he thought at that time that they were composed of 'globules'; later he changed his mind: 'Although I showed the hair to several learned gentlemen, who always agreed with me that it consisted of no other parts than globules, especially after we had distinctly seen that the cortex of the hair of elks and stags consisted of globules, I was not contented with such observations. I took the hair of my beard, after it had been shaved first, second, third and fourth days and observed, that the little particles which we saw through the common microscope (which yet were very good) and which appeared round, were indeed irregular, and lay very closely pressed upon one another' (this was probably the scales covering the surface of the hairs) ' . . . I then examined the roots of several hairs and clearly saw that the whole root, except the cortex, consisted of little strings. These strings or pipes do not lie everywhere stretched out in a straight line, but in some places are somewhat crooked.'

Evidently Leeuwenhoek saw the rows of cornified cells which, arranged length-wise, form the interior part of the hair. Here once again, we have an example of Leeuwenhoek correcting, sometimes after a very long period of further investigation, his mistakes; at first he denied the existence of pores in the skin, but in a letter (September 17th, 1717) written when he was eighty-five, he described how he made sections of his own skin and saw pores (obviously the openings of the sweat glands). The observations listed above, on muscle, nerves, capillaries and blood cells, bones and teeth surely will be more than enough to convince the most sceptical reader that Leeuwenhoek was one of the great histologists.

CHAPTER SIX

Leeuwenhoek and the Study of Entomology

Pliny remarked that the wonders of nature were greatest in the smallest things; the small insects are no exception to this. Among the first figures of microscopical objects are those of insects. Hooke, in his *Micrographia* (1665) pictures a louse so highly magnified that the figure is about fourteen inches long; Malpighi followed with his famous *De Bombyce* in 1669, and in the same year Swammerdam published his *Historia generalis*. Redi's work, *Experimentia circa generationem Insectorum* had already appeared in an Italian edition, but the Latin translation was not published until 1671.

Although Leeuwenhoek knew of the work of Hooke, Malpighi and Redi, he could read only Swammerdam's work; in the other cases he had to be content with studying the plates. The famous entomologist Bodenheimer has pointed out that Leeuwenhoek always tried to solve his problems by means of comparative studies: and what is more surprising is the certainty of his conclusions which were almost all based on entirely new observations. Cole (1937) states that Leeuwenhoek studied sixty-seven species of insects (as well as one myriapod, eleven arachnids, and ten crustaceans, making a total of eighty-nine different species of arthropods!). It is only possible to give a few examples of his researches in this field, so we have chosen to describe his studies on the plant louse, the flea and the corn-weevil.

The plant louse or aphid

The first letter in which Leeuwenhoek mentions this insect (Cole says it is *Myzus ribes*) is dated July 10th, 1695. Leeuwenhoek begins as if he were speaking to a friend, confessing an error which had never been printed before and which he could have easily kept secret. 'Having frequently observed the leaves at the ends of the young shoots of gooseberry trees, and also on cherry and peach trees, to be very much contracted, and, as it were, rolled up, by which means the growth of these trees was impeded; and perceiving, at the same time, many ants on the leaves so contracted, I at first adopted the vulgar opinion, that the ants alone were the cause of the contraction of the leaves.

'I therefore determined to examine for what purpose the ants resorted to those young leaves, and what was the cause of the leaves being contracted; in doing which, I saw that the contracted leaves, and especially those of the gooseberry trees, were covered with a great number of dark-coloured animalcules, and that those which were most fully grown were about the size of a half-grown louse, and were of a darker or blacker colour than the smaller ones. . . . Upon sight of these creatures, I concluded that the ants resorted to the contracted leaves for no other purpose than to devour these animalcules on them.' (It was not until 1810 that P. Huber discovered that the ants lick up the sweet exudations of the plant-lice.) Leeuwenhoek looked for their eggs, but he was unable to find them. 'But all my search was to no purpose, at which I was most surprised. This seemed to favour the opinion of those who will have it, that small living creatures are produced spontaneously, but such a notion appeared to me altogether impossible, though, at the same time, I was at a loss how to investigate the generation of these creatures. At length I determined to open some of the largest of them, in the hope of finding eggs in their bodies; but instead of   135

eggs, I found, not without great admiration, young animalcules in the bodies of the larger ones, and in the shape so like
the parent, that one drop of water cannot be more like the
other, and I extracted not a single young one, but four, completely formed from the same parent. Hereupon I judged
that it would be most expedient to cut off all twigs and leaves
of the peaches, cherries and gooseberry trees which were
infested with these creatures, and throw them into the water
to drown them, and try whether I should not after be less
infested with these vermin.' Leeuwenhoek thought that these
animalcules would hibernate on the trunk or branches of the
trees: 'therefore, in January, after a long frost and rain
following, I cut a branch from the gooseberry tree, and
examining it by microscope, I saw several of these animalcules, which all seemed fully grown. They were not only
dead, but the hinder parts of their bodies were perforated
with a round hole, and their entrails gone, whence I gathered
that provident Nature had assigned these creatures their
enemies, to prevent their species increasing too fast, and also
for the sustenance of other animals.' This idea of an equili-
brium in nature is often expressed by Leeuwenhoek. In May
of the following year he found twenty-one young inside a
single animal, and he made an experiment. 'On the 20th of
May, I cut off three branches of this year's growth from a
gooseberry tree, on which branches I was certain there was
no animalcule of this species; these I put into a vessel of
water, and on the tops of two of them I put two, and on the
third branch three of those animalcules, which I deemed by
their size to be females, in order to see how soon, and to
what degree, they would bring forth young: and in twenty-
four hours, two of these produced nine young ones, and a
third, six. From a branch with flowers some ants were
brought into the house. These crept into the branches
and killed some of the animalcules. Hereupon I killed all
those ants, and placed the vessel containing the branches

in a dish full of water to defend the access to it from ants.'

Leeuwenhoek was doubtful whether the damage done by the ants was outweighed by their usefulness in eating the plant-lice in the spring. On further examination, he saw not only the plant-lice, but also 'flies, which have four wings. I could not, at first, think they were produced from other animalcules, but upon examining them with the microscope, I found the bodies of both of them to be very similar, and, after several repeated observations, I saw the first mentioned animalcules had, on each side of their bodies, a long white protuberant part, which upon examination I found to be the future wings. I also opened the bodies of several of the flies, and in them saw young ones of the same form, and in like numbers, as the other animalcules, all which plainly proved to me that these animalcules, commonly called gooseberry-lice, are changed into flies.' He worked out the time they took to propagate and found that 'within thirteen days after they are produced from the parent, they breed within them sixty young ones, many of which can be seen completely formed . . . and lastly changed into flying animals which continue to bring forth young; this must appear wonderful, and be a confirmation of the principle, that all living creatures deduce their origin from those which were formed at the Beginning.' Leeuwenhoek had made the important discoveries that the plant-lice were both *polymorphic* and *viviparous* (i.e. they have different forms of the same species, and do not lay eggs but produce their young alive). (Plate 15.) He always took a great pleasure in the wonders of Nature; this is apparent in this present case for he wrote: 'In the hind part of its body this animalcule has two parts . . . and from these organs I often saw a small drop of very transparent liquor issue. This small drop exhibited a very pleasant spectacle to me, for, when removed a little further from the microscope it had the effect of another microscope, showing the objects,   137

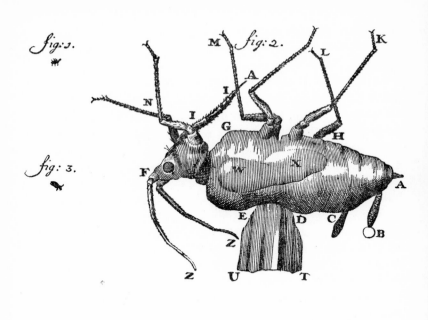

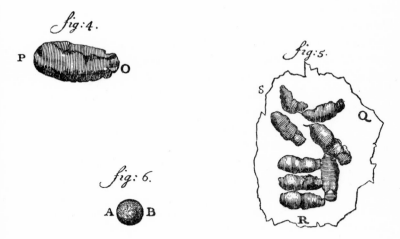

PLATE 15 *Plant lice. 5, the unborn young in the female; 6, eye*

as houses, steeples and the like, inverted, and so minute and delicate in their appearance, that it scarce could be believed.'

In the same letter Leeuwenhoek described another important discovery: 'These pieces of leaves, whereon the dead creatures (=green plant-lice) lay, I put into a great glass tube, covered at both ends with fine linen; for I concluded that the death of these lice was occasioned by another creature, or an egg thrust into their bodies, where it receives food and growth, and then makes its way out of their bodies again. I had shut up these dead lice about eight days, when I observed two little flies, of quite another kind, in wings, colour and shape, leaping about the glass. I shifted these flies into another glass tube, where I had before put six green lice, which I had taken from the leaf of a currant-tree and those of the most fully grown.

'These flies, as soon as ever they came near the said lice, brought the hinder part of their body, which was pretty long, between their feet, and stretched their body so far out, that their tail making a kind of semi-circle with the rest of the body (as you may see in the draught annexed [Plate 16]) stood out beyond their heads, and in this manner they insinuated their tail into the bodies of the worms (=plant-lice), and this the flies did in a short time to all the worms that they came near to: but that which was most marked in this action was, that in this conjunction they never touched the lice . . . nay, one would say that they were afraid of these lice as if they would devour them; and as they entered the bodies of the lice they made a quivering motion or shaking with their tail.' In 1660, the Middelburg painter, Goedaert, had noticed that not a butterfly but another insect sometimes issued from a caterpillar. He found this 'extraordinary remarkable,' but he could not solve the mystery: Leeuwenhoek, however, after five years of study had found the solution and he described the infection and growth of the internal 139 parasite *Aphidius* in a way which surely merits the word 'classical'!

The corn-beetle or weevil and the means to preserve corn from infection

Although it was usual for Leeuwenhoek to discuss several topics in each letter, and to return often to the same subjects

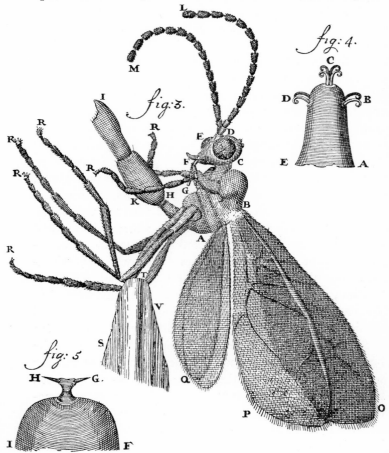

PLATE 16 *Parasite of plant lice*

in the course of his life, in the case of the 'weevil' (*Calandria granaria* L., an insect about three mm. long) he devotes the greater part of his letter dated August 6th, 1687, to this animal and only mentions it again twice (letters of March 7th, 1692 and June 16th, 1700). This subject therefore gives us an excellent example of Leeuwenhoek's method of tackling a problem and shows us how he was essentially a practical man who, having found a solution to a problem, drew from it a conclusion which could be applied in practice.

'I have heard it strongly argued, that the weevil or corn-beetle (which is a very noxious insect, well-known to corn dealers and bakers in this country) is produced by what is called equivocal or spontaneous generation, that is to say, from inanimate substances without any parent. The principal reasons alleged in support of this opinion are, that we often find this insect in a new granary, where wheat was never kept before, and therefore it is deemed a necessary conclusion, that weevils are not propagated by the ordinary course of generation. Again, it is said that we may open many grains of wheat, which are sound and uninjured, so that no mark of a hole or perforation shall be discernible on the outside, yet within the grains shall be found perfectly formed and living weevils.

'The answer which I have given to these arguments has been that these little animals, may by ourselves, be removed from one granary to another without our knowledge: for supposing the person employed to remove corn, to have come out of a barn or granary, infested with weevils, he may easily carry some grains of corn containing them, or some of the insects themselves, sticking about his clothes, or in his shoes, and thus remove them into a granary where none had ever been. Beside, the ship, waggon, or cart, employed to carry corn, may be infested with weevils, by having carried grain in which they abound, and thus from a few of these insects, 141 multitudes may be produced by the ordinary course of generation.

'But in order fully to investigate the truth of this, I desired the persons who argued this matter with me, to bring me the first weevils they themselves should find (it being then the winter-season); and on the 13th of March I received some grains of wheat (many of which had the insides eaten away) mixed with the weevils. I took three glasses, in each of which I put six, eight or nine weevils and eight, ten or twelve grains of wheat, which wheat I was assured could not be infected, because it had been kept for several months, closely covered up in my study. In a fourth glass I put some weevils without any wheat, but this last mode of experiment I afterwards rejected, observing that in the space of twelve days they all died. As to the other three glasses the weather being cold, and observing the animals, for the most part, to lie motionless, I put them in a leather case which I always carried about with me. I, at first, entertained the idea that the weevil, like the silk-worm's moth and many other insects, did not, whilst in that shape, take any food: but herein I found myself mistaken, and observed that the weevil not only feeds upon wheat, but it can excavate or scoop out the whole contents of every grain, and creep about in the inside, being provided with a beak, or trunk of a great length, in proportion to the size of its body, at the extremity of which are exceedingly small organs, or instruments like teeth, and with these it can bore through the outward husk of wheat.' (Plate 17.)

'At a fortnight's end, on the 27th of March, I observed some of the weevils coupled together, the female carrying the male, and strolling about with it. . . . On the 10th of June, I observed lying among the weevils and the wheat, two short and thick little maggots, one of them about the size of a large grain of sand, and the other about one-fourth part larger: seeing this, I opened one of the glasses in which I had enclosed

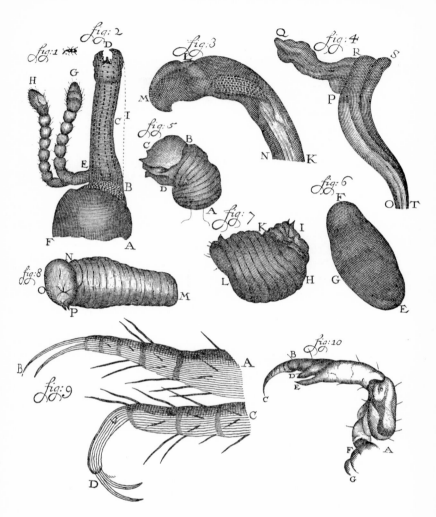

PLATE 17 *Corn-weevil.* 2, *mouth-parts*; 3, *male genital organ*;
5, 7, 8, *larvæ*; 6, *egg*; 9, *leg of a louse, drawing of*
Griendelius; 10, *leg of a louse, drawing of Leeuwenhoek*

six weevils, and examined the different grains of wheat that had been put in with them, and found two of them to be entirely hollow and empty; from another of the grains, which by the external appearance was the least eaten or consumed, but had many small perforations not discernible by the naked eye, I drew out a perfectly formed weevil, which was of a yellow colour, whereas those which were first brought to me were of a deep red, almost approaching black.

'In another grain of the wheat, I found a weevil, of a very pale or white colour, with its claws, and beak or trunk, lying close to the body, in exact order as we see the wings or legs of a silk-worm's chrysalis or aurelia, when it is almost arrived at the state of a flying insect. In other grains of the wheat I found maggots of different sizes. . . . Examining the other glasses, I found some of the grains of wheat perforated with little holes, and others half eaten. Some of the weevils which had been shut up in these glasses I opened, and in one of these I found five white eggs, which I conceived to be of their full size: in others I observed eggs, some of which were arrived to maturity, and others gradually less and less mature.

'Hence I concluded, that whereas the silk-worm's moth, living only a few days, in that time lays a multitude of eggs and then dies: the weevil, which every day produced but a few eggs, is on the other hand a long-lived animal, and by this means may be as prolific as the silk-worm or other insects: for the weevils which I am now treating of, were all alive the preceding summer. As to the two maggots which I, at first, found in the glass among the wheat, I had no doubt that they had fallen out of the grains wherein they had first been deposited, by reason that those grains had been rather too much eaten away before the eggs were laid in them. . . . I think it very probable that the large trunk with which this insect is provided, is given to it of such a length

that it may be enabled to bore a small deep hole in every

grain of wheat, and therein deposit an egg: for if a weevil were to lay its eggs on the outside of a grain, and a maggot should be hatched from it, such a maggot could not possibly pierce the husk of the wheat. Again, were such a weevil to lay more than one egg in one grain, and all these eggs produced maggots, they would hinder each other's growth, for want of having sufficient nourishment.

'I observed in opening one grain in which a small hole had been made, and out of which I took only one single egg, that round about that part where the egg was placed, the mealy substance of the wheat had been loosened . . . both to make a soft place for the egg to lie in, and also, that the minute maggot might find this soft and loosened meal prepared for its first feeding on.

'Some of these maggots I placed in glasses by themselves, and observed them gradually to assume the form of weevils, the beak, horns and claws appearing by degrees, and the colour also changing from a white to a yellow and then to the red colour of the weevil.' Leeuwenhoek put three females into a glass without grains of wheat and so obtained some eggs, which produced the kind of maggots mentioned above after about seven days. 'These maggots have very little strength to move from place to place. . . . In my opinion it would be impossible for the maggot lying outside a grain to procure nourishment and become a perfect weevil.' He concluded: 'These things considered, we may be fully satisfied respecting the reason why, in corn, which is frequently moved and shifted, the weevil can increase but little: for supposing one of these insects to have pierced and prepared two or three grains ready to deposit its eggs, and soon afterwards the corn is moved and spread about, the animal must leave such an egg on the outside of the corn, where the young maggot must perish.' Leeuwenhoek also gave a remarkable proof of his manual skill, by mentioning in his letter that he had succeeded in dissecting out the male

145

K

organs of such a small beetle and finding in them the spermatozoa. He continued: 'I trust that these observations and
experiments will prove that weevils cannot be produced
otherwise than by propagation, that is to say, by copulating
and laying eggs, from which eggs, maggots are produced,
and finally these maggots are changed into weevils. . . . And
although this is a very minute animal, yet its species must
have been continued in this way from its first being formed
at the creation: and would it be otherwise, namely that from
inanimate matter this or any other animal should be produced, that would be a miracle; and such formation or new
creation must be continually derived from the Almighty
Creator.

'Probably some people may wish me to inquire into the
propagation of other minute animals, but for the present I
leave the prosecution of these matters to those who may
choose to bestow as much labour thereon as I have done in
this examination of the weevil, assuring them that my
observations are the result of more than four months' application to the subject.'

The grain moth

Leeuwenhoek could not, however, resist the temptation to
examine the 'wolf or grain moth' (*Tinea granaria*), which
common opinion held to be produced from corruption. He
found the eggs, saw the little moths copulating, and then
(March 7th, 1692) made the following experiment: 'I took a
round glass vessel, large enough to hold six pints of water,
and I put in it eight living moths newly taken. In the orifice
of this vessel I set fire to the fourth part of a grain of sulphur,
and as soon as the moths began to feel the vapour they
fluttered about the glass with great violence, though but for
a short time, for they all fell to the bottom, and after a
little motion in their feet, they died. . . . From the size of
this glass, I computed what quantity of sulphur would be

requisite to fumigate a granary twenty-four feet long, sixteen broad, and eight high, and I reckoned that half a pound would be sufficient for the purpose. After this, I fumigated a granary, in which were eight loads of wheat, and a great number of moths flying about. For this purpose, I took pieces of sulphur, each containing about a quarter of a pound, prepared in the same manner as is done by wine-merchants to fumigate their casks.' Here, his professional knowledge as a wine-gauger helped him in his experiments.

'These pieces of sulphur I suspended by a brass wire, in a tall earthen vessel, with a narrow top, and placed the vessel in an earthen dish to prevent any danger of fire. This apparatus I set in the middle of the wheat, and as soon as the sulphur began to burn, I retired out of the granary and shut the door. In a large granary, two or three of these vessels might be used. Two days afterwards, I visited the granary, and then I saw several moths still clinging to the wall and beams, but before the fumigation I believe there were ten times as many. And I accounted for these moths still being found alive, either because many of the panes of glass in the windows were broken, through which much of the smoke of the sulphur had escaped, or else, that the moths which I saw now, had come out of their aurelia-state after the fumigation was over; for I am well assured, that so long as the moths are enclosed in their aurelia-case, the smoke of sulphur cannot do them any injury. Therefore it will be necessary for those who choose to fumigate their granaries in the manner I have recommended, to begin the operation as soon as ever the moths appear, that they may be prevented from laying their eggs, and also to continue the use of it for some days, indeed as long as any moths are to be seen, because these creatures do not all come out of their aurelia-state at the same time. The expense of fumigating is no object, for a pound of sulphur may be bought for a trifle, and it is in no sort injurious to the wheat, nor is it prejudicial to the   147 health of any person, but rather salubrious.' After untangling the life-cycle of this little animal, Leeuwenhoek gave a description of several of its organs and then asks: 'Can this moth, I say adorned with so many beauties, be produced from corruption? For in a word, in this little creature, contemptible as it seems to us, there shines forth so much perfection and skill in the formation, as to exceed what we observe in larger animals.' His admiration for the little animals and the perfection of their fine structure was one of the arguments which led him to reject the idea of spontaneous generation.

The life-history of the flea

In olden times a magnifying glass was often called a 'pulicarium,' so it does not surprise us that Leeuwenhoek should study the little brown animal which gave its name to this instrument (*Pulex*=flea); indeed, he refers to it in no fewer than fifteen different letters written between 1677 and 1717.

The famous Father Kircher wrote at this time that fleas generate in the dust of the floors, from their own excrement. He added that some persons had a different opinion, but 'if they should have had magnifying glasses,' they would have agreed with him. Jan Swammerdam had published his *Historia generalis* in 1669, in which he gave his theory of preformation and at the same time gave a new classification of fleas, based on their development and metamorphosis. He placed the flea in his 'order 1' (loc. cit. p. 74), as he thought that it underwent all its transformations in the 'nit' or egg. With a magnifying glass he could see how it was first white, and gradually became red or black.

Leeuwenhoek says in his letter of October 5th, 1677: 'Apparently Monsieur Swammerdam has taken the excrements for the eggs.' He kept several fleas and saw the white eggs after twenty-four hours; he opened these eggs hoping, as Swammerdam had done, to see the young animals, but he

148

found only 'globules' (=yolk). He then put the eggs in a little box in his trouser-pocket and saw to his astonishment 'little grubs or maggots,' which he could breed and see transform into pupae.

In November 1677, he looked for the spermatozoa, but he was unable to find them; in 1680, however, he discovered the testes: 'I repeatedly convinced myself that each flea had two of such vesicles, although in some fleas I found but one vesicle. Maybe I now and then, in cutting open the flea, broke a vesicle, which would account for my seeing only one.' With his extraordinary fairness, Leeuwenhoek once more confessed a presumed fault. He continued: 'But what astonished me most of all and surpassed my comprehension more than anything, was that I discovered such large animals in the semen of this animal. But then I have constantly found that the animalcules in male seed are not at all in proportion to the size of the animals.'

Swammerdam died before he could read this letter, but he read the one dated 5th October, 1677, for in his *Biblia Naturae* we find the following words: 'If it did, the insect must belong to the third order and by no means to the first.' He intended to investigate this again, but he never carried out his intention.

In 1683, Leeuwenhoek returned to the study of the flea, and he saw the flesh-fibres (see Chapter Five): 'In my letter of March 3rd, 1682, I wrote about the structure of flesh, and fish muscles, adding that I intended to examine the structure of the flesh of little animals (here=little mammals). But I changed my intention and first tried to experiment on a flea, considering that, if I could discover flesh-fibres in it, we may be sure that all the flesh muscles of animals are of the same structure. Not once, but at least fifty times, I have clearly and distinctly observed the flesh-fibres taken from the breast of a flea, with which its legs were partly united to the breast, and have seen that they also had those circular shrinkages, 149 like those of the flesh and fish fibres I mentioned before.' He added: 'Once more I have taken the testicles of a flea, this time with less difficulty'; obviously his powers of micro-dissection had increased.

He also saw the tracheae, 'the ringed veins' (which he had previously mentioned in 1680). 'I felt convinced that they were not respiratory vessels, but imagined that they were arteries, for they not only surrounded the flea's entrails, but lay spread in great numbers among and on the eggs. I felt the more convinced because I noticed that the skin of the head, a little below the eyes, continually contracted and pro-truded, the reason being, I imagined, that this was the place of respiration.'

As always, Leeuwenhoek made a distinction between the facts and his interpretation of them. In this case he was mis-taken, his unitarian conception of Nature caused him to believe that respiratory organs must be the same in both mammals and fleas! At the spot indicated by Leeuwenhoek there is a salivary pump associated with the intestinal canal, and it may have been this that he saw.

Leeuwenhoek did not succeed in rearing the maggots, and therefore he 'took grubs which he supposed to be fully grown, and observed that they spent eight to ten days spin-ning and then shed their skin, and became a pupa.' This was a mistake which he must also have made in 1677. It was in October, 1693, that he succeeded in rearing fleas from the eggs to the adults. He was successful with the fleas of the pigeon (*Ceratophyllus columbae* Steph.) and later with the human flea. He reared the larvae of this species by feeding them with dead flies, 'which they devoured eagerly.' On July 6th, the larvae hatched from the egg, and on the thirtieth of the same month the flea 'jumped about in the glass' (Plate 18).

Leeuwenhoek also noticed that a flea has its enemies too! 'On several occasions I contrived to prevent the maggots

150

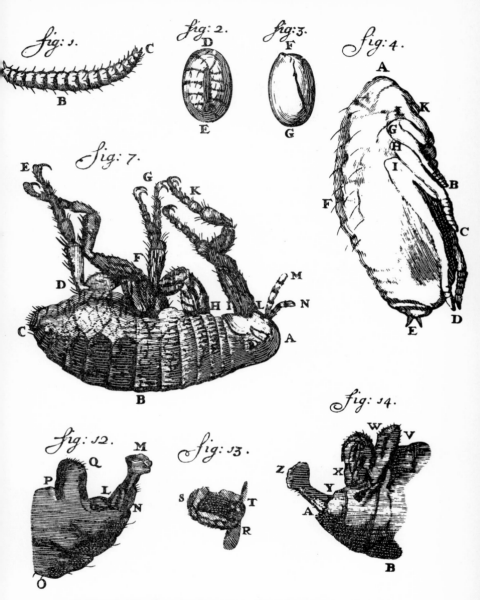

PLATE 18 *The flea, development and anatomy.* 12, *male genital organ* (*see overleaf*)

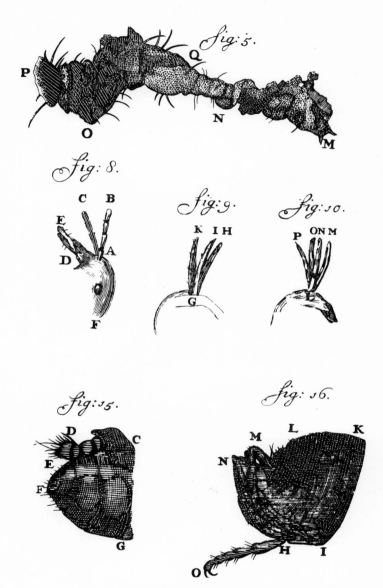

PLATE 18 *The flea, development and anatomy (cont.)*

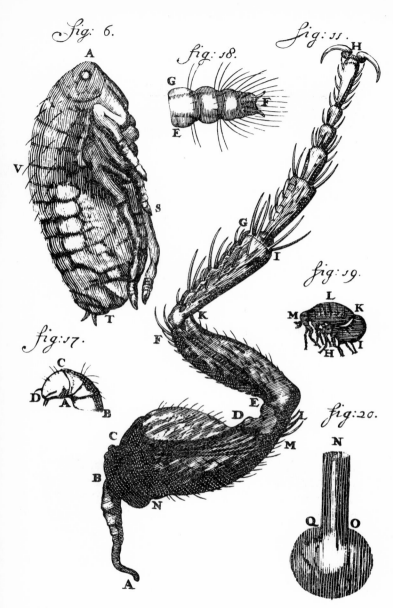

fig: 6.

fig: 18.

fig: 11.

fig: 17.

fig: 19.

fig: 20.

10, *mouth-parts*; 15, *female genital organ*

enclosing themselves completely in their webs, in order that I might the more easily discern their alteration into a chrysalis or aurelia. But how oftensoever I viewed them after they had ceased eating, and their change approached, I could only perceive that they placed themselves in the same position as they had lain in the egg. But examining them in the afternoon in this posture, I found upon looking at them three hours afterwards, that one of them was changed into a chrysalis. Upon viewing another of them through the microscope, I perceived a mite upon its body, where it remained some time, and another larger mite running through the glass, whereupon I concluded, that at the time these worms are in their state of change and unable to defend themselves, the mites will seize and feed upon them. After this worm had thus lain for some hours, I saw that its body was somewhat contracted, whereupon placing it before the microscope, I perceived three holes pierced in its body, part of its skin stripped off, and the body beginning to dry away. Hereupon I began to consider, that this web or covering spun by the flea, worm or maggot is necessary to it, and that without it those creatures could not easily be propagated; for there are seldom any fragments of food or the bodies of small animals lying about our houses, but they are immediately found out by mites who come to feed upon them.'

Leeuwenhoek thus dissected the mouth parts, the genitalia, and saw the copulation of the flea; M. Beier wrote that Lundblad was the first to see the copulation of this animal, but old Antoni described it nearly two and a half centuries before him!

The compound eyes of insects; galls and hyperparasites

It is not possible to consider in much detail Leeuwenhoek's
numerous descriptions of the anatomy of various insects, but

his enquiry into the structure of their compound eyes was so remarkable that it must be mentioned.

It is known that Galileo in 1610 showed an English visitor that the eyes of insects had many facets; Stelluti (1625) gave drawings of bees, showing their compound eyes clearly. Hooke and the other microscopists of Leeuwenhoek's time had also studied this organ, and Swammerdam gives a good drawing of the eye of a bee and also of a transverse section of it. This work must have been done before 1680 (and presumably before 1673), but as it was not published until 1737 it remained unknown to Leeuwenhoek.

In the letter of April 30th, 1694, and again in November of the same year, Leeuwenhoek studied the eyes of the dragonfly (*Libellula*). He cleaned the cornea on the inner side and found that each element was six-sided and formed a segment of a sphere (Plate 19). A lighted candle viewed through the cornea and correctly focused ('a little more from the lens as was the right distance to see the cornea itself') was reproduced inverted by each element. Under these conditions, as Cole remarks, Leeuwenhoek's microscope would give an inverted image. (If any one is eager to see this phenomenon for himself, it is advisable to mount the cornea in the usual manner but to include a little air underneath it.) Leeuwenhoek could even see the trembling of the flame in the image produced by the eye. 'The great tower or steeple of our New Church in Delft, which is three hundred feet high and about seven hundred and fifty feet distant from my house, when viewed through these optical organs, appeared no larger than the point of a small needle seen by the naked eye; and from this it may easily be seen how minute the optic nerves (=the ommatidia, or component parts of the compound eye) must appear to me.' In the neighbouring houses he could see not only the buildings, but the doors and windows, and he could tell whether the windows were open or shut. He explained this by saying: 'The focus of each may   155

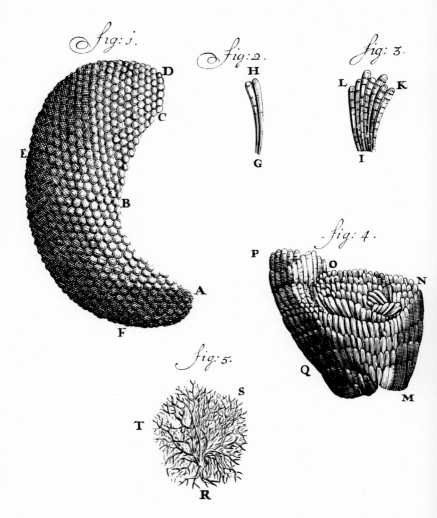

fig: 1.

D

C

E

B

A

F

Fig: 2.

H

G

fig: 3.

L

K

I

fig: 4.

P

O

N

Q

M

fig: 5.

S

T

R

PLATE 19 *The insect eye. 5, brain of a little fly*

(if I am allowed the expression) become united in one point, as happens when two convex lenses are placed one before the other in a frame.' In the same letter (May 9th, 1698), he gave an account of his study of a beetle. In England, he said, it was a proverbial expression when any person was reproached for his blindness or stupidity, to say that he was as blind as a beetle, under the impression that this animal is devoid of sight. He then calculated that such a beetle has $2 \times 3,181$ eyes! Leeuwenhoek was firmly convinced that he had demonstrated experimentally that each element formed a complete picture, which is, as Cole says, 'a remarkable anticipation of Johannes Müller's theory.' When Leeuwenhoek was asked in 1700 whether such an animal would not see as many independent images as it had eyes, he merely said that we with two eyes do not see things double, so the dragonfly with 25,088 eyes will also have only one image.

Leeuwenhoek was very proud of his discovery that galls on oak were produced by insects, and in the mezzotint by Verkolje (1686) the oak-galls are lying on the table before him. When, in 1701, he studied the willow-galls (produced by the saw-fly *Nematus gallicus*) for the second time, he discovered the 'hyperparasite'. Mr. R. B. Benson informed Professor Cole that this was *Pimpla (Epiurus) vesicaria*, an Ichneumon which is the most common parasite of *Nematus*. Leeuwenhoek, having seen the eggs of the hyperparasite, thought that the gall was pierced by the hyperparasite which then laid its eggs in the interior of the gall. After hatching into small larvae, these would then parasitize the larva of the gall insect which was already within the gall. Cole remarks: 'Leeuwenhoek probably never saw the adult saw-fly. . . . At this point Leeuwenhoek drops the investigation, but not before he had reduced to intelligible terms the biology of the internal parasites, and given the clearest lead to his successors.'

It seems clear from the examples of his work quoted above that Leeuwenhoek was an experimental scientist, who reared the animals he studied, and was eager to apply his fundamental studies to every-day life; in the field of entomology he not only made important basic discoveries, but also realized their applications, so virtually founding the study of applied entomology.

CHAPTER SEVEN

Leeuwenhoek Studies
the 'Lower Animals'

The discovery of a famous animal (HYDRA VULGARIS)

One of Leeuwenhoek's discoveries which was almost neglected in his own time, but was afterwards considered to be very important, was that of the fresh-water polyp (*Hydra*) in 1702, an animal which was to become famous as a result of the work of Abraham Trembley (1744).

Leeuwenhoek writes: 'Further, I discovered a little animal whose body was at times long, at times drawn up short, and to the middle of whose body (where I imagined the undermost part of its belly was) a still lesser animalcule of the same kind seemed fast by its hinder end. Such a little animal, because of its wonderful structure and manner of propagation, I have had drawn, and at least twice as big as it looks to the naked eye when you see it in the water and attached to the root of a bit of duckweed. Fig. 4, ABCDEFG (here reproduced as part of Plate 20), shows this creature, whereof A is the hind end it hangs on by, while at CDE are shown its eight horns (though another a bit smaller had six horns) as it looked when it had straightened itself out, for otherwise it can scarce reach to a quarter of this length; and its horns seemed to my eye to be made in so marvellous a manner, that the draughtsman's art is not competent to portray them, though the artist did his best to draw a small bit of a horn, as shown at KLM in fig. 5 (see Plate 20). In fig. 4 at BH, is shown a little animal

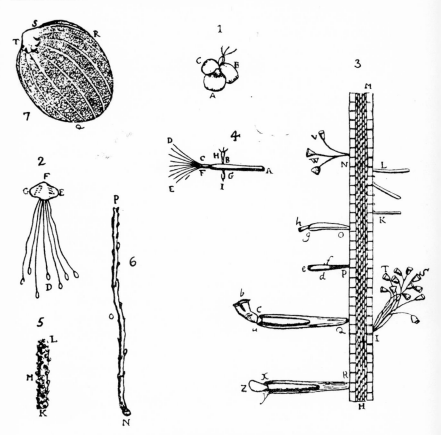

PLATE 20 *Duckweed and microscopic creatures.*
7, rotifers and vorticella; 4, 5, 6, Hydra

that is coming out of the first one; and formerly, when I saw
such a little animal fixed to a bigger one, I imagined that it
was only a young animalcule attached by chance to a big one;
but by nicer attention to the matter, I saw it was a reproduction: for I observed that whereas the second animalcule,
at the time when I first recognized that it was really one, had
only four very short little horns, yet after the lapse of sixteen

hours I saw that its body and its horns had increased in bigness, and four hours later still, I saw it had forsaken its
mother.

'When I discovered the animal aforesaid, I also perceived
that, on the other side of the body of the first animal, there
was situated a little round knob, which I did see getting
bigger from time to time for the next few hours (as shown
between G and I in the figure); and at last it appeared as a
pointed structure, which had grown so far in bigness in the
course of thirteen or fourteen hours, that you could make
out two little horns upon it. After the lapse of another four
and twenty hours, this last mentioned animalcule had four
horns, and the other two much bigger; and these last the
little animal struck out at full length, or pulled in short. And
another three hours later, this little animal was gone from its
mother.

'I tried to trace this reproduction further, and for this
purpose took the duckweed away from the animalcule, so
that I could follow it better; but next day that animalcule
not only lay dead, but its horns and a piece of its hind end
were all gone, having rotted away, so to speak.

'Another little animal that had brought forth two young
ones, not only had its body laden with many other animalcules (=the common 'polyp-louse,' *Trichodina pediculus*)
which are flat beneath, and roundish above, and which I
have discovered in most other kinds of water and which are
hardly a thousandth of the animals which they crawl on with
their little feet, and cause annoyance to; but a much bigger
sort of animalcule whose bodies were roundish, so pestered
one of these little animals, not only getting her body, but
also clinging to her horns, that in spite of all the struggles
she made with her horns and body, she could not shake it
off; and I noticed afterwards that the little animal had lost
one of her horns.' (This must have been the Protozoan
Kerona.)

161

L

'What seemed to me remarkable and wonderful, was that these little animals would oft-times let down their horns so far, that you would think, on seeing them through the microscope, that they were several fathoms long. At one time or another I let the draughtsman have a look at the horns as they were being stretched out, or anon pulled in; and with me he was forced to exclaim: "What wonders are these!" For as the creature pulled in its horns, they became perfectly round, and the closer they got to the head, the thicker they became, and when they were pulled right in, they formed a still bigger round blob.

'I then charged the draughtsman to draw, as well as he was able to, a small part of a horn when stuck out, which is here shown at NOP (fig. 6, Plate 20). On this part are shown the knob-like lumps, which are also to be seen in fig. 5, KLM. These lumps look to me as though they were made up of seven round globules; to wit, one in the middle, which sticks up a bit above the others, and the rest lying round it in a rosette' (=the nematocysts and their cnidocils, organs which were not understood by either Leeuwenhoek or Trembley).

'Now if we consider what a lot of instruments must be contained in a little piece like fig. 6, in order that it may not only be stretched out, but also drawn in and moved around, and with as many bends and knots in it too, as you might make in a piece of string; so must we wonder all the more at such a contrivance. And who knows but what every knot-like part may not also itself be furnished with yet other organs, whereby they are set in motion.'

Dobell remarks: 'No animal which reproduces asexually by budding was known at that date; and the sensation caused by similar observations of Trembley and others, nearly half a century later, is in strange contrast with the apparent indifference which greeted Leeuwenhoek's discovery.' This discovery, which was made when Leeuwenhoek was seventy, has been quoted in full, as it merits more attention than it usually receives. It is worth mentioning that Leeuwenhoek discovered his *Hydra* at Delft, which is only a few miles from The Hague where Trembley found his specimens. Leeuwenhoek's description gives a vivid impression of his admiration for the wonders of Nature which he discovered, and it shows once more that he thought that all animals and animalcules had essentially the same structure. In this respect Trembley had a much more modern outlook; in the case of *Hydra*, however, Leeuwenhoek specifically stated that it was its manner of propagation which led him to communicate his observations to the Royal Society.

Leeuwenhoek's observations on molluscs

As Leeuwenhoek had a very wide interest in all living organisms, he often examined all the species he was able to obtain; Cole says that Leeuwenhoek studied eleven species of mollusc and mention of them occurs in fourteen of his letters. In one of his first letters (dated March 26th, 1675) he remarked: 'I observed two or three small pearls, after having broken the same into pieces, and saw that the same are composed of very small globules; the growth of the pearl takes place with scales, in the manner of an onion.' This was written during the period when Leeuwenhoek believed in the universal existence of globules. In this case this is not surprising, as pearls consist of a number of concentric layers of mother-of-pearl, separated by thin strata of organic matter (conchiolin). In the case of old pearls, this often results in scaling as Leeuwenhoek described. Mother-of-pearl consists of microscopic crystals of aragonite which are prismatic and are of a round or irregular polygonal cross-section. Their diameter is mostly about $1-1\frac{1}{2}\mu$, while their length is sometimes as much as 10μ. In all probability it is these which Leeuwenhoek was referring to when he wrote of 'globules.'

163

His most interesting observations were made on the oyster, the sea-mussel and the fresh-water mussel; it was the generation of these creatures which principally interested him, but he soon discovered the ciliary motion on their gills. (Cilia are fine protoplasmic threads which project from the surface of a cell. When such cells are arranged in sheets, they form a ciliated epithelium, and here the cilia may be seen to beat in a co-ordinated rhythm.) Leeuwenhoek had seen the cilia of the Protozoa (see Chapter Three), and now he writes on March 3rd, 1682: 'I have made good use of the time when oysters come over to us from England for a short time, and was astonished to see the uncommonly great stir and movement of the beards (=gills) of the oysters. And though I took very small pieces from the beards, even so small that a few hundreds of such parts would not make a grain of coarse sand, yet, there was in such a small separated part of the beard such great movement that one could not comprehend it, for such a small part reminded me of a shrimp with its continually moving legs or again of a lobster; and one would have sworn that it was not part of the beard, but an animal itself.' Although Antoni de Heide is often called the discoverer of the ciliary motion (his book is dated October, 1683, and was published in 1684), Leeuwenhoek's description was published in Hooke's *Philosophical Collections* (London, 1682) so that it seems that Leeuwenhoek has the priority.

As usual, he looked for the spermatozoa, and in April, 1694, he thought he had found the eggs. He 'imagined' that there was an ovipositor (an organ through which the eggs are laid) as the presumed eggs were placed on the outsides of the shell. He had, in fact, discovered a Bryozoan (*Membranipora*), an animal which belongs to quite a different phylum of the animal kingdom, and which he took to be the eggs of the sea-mussel. As Cole (1937) says, 'This is one of the few serious mistakes made by Leeuwenhoek.'

164   In the same letter, Leeuwenhoek wrote: 'I have been in-

formed that a book is published at Rome, by a learned Jesuit, named Philippo Bonanni, wherein he maintains that animalcules can be produced out of inanimate substances, such as mud or sand, by spontaneous generation, according to the doctrine of Aristotle.' As mussels and oysters live in the mud, this stimulated him to continue his observations. On the 18th September, 1695, he wrote: 'The young mussels, when come to maturity are easily carried to other muddy shores on the coast, in places where for many years before no mussels were found.'

Leeuwenhoek also saw the young mussels in the 'eggs' and in later years he found the young in the gills of the oyster and discovered that they were capable of swimming when they are discharged into the water. He measured them and calculated that the breadth of 120 would be equal to one inch, and therefore a globe with a diameter of one inch would contain 1,728,000 young oysters.

In 1696, he turned to an examination of the fresh-water mussel (*Anodonta*), placing them 'into an earthen vessel, with a flat bottom, and poured on them some of the same water in which they were taken.

'At the end of the month of August, upon opening six of these mussels, I found many eggs within them, which were so perfect that I could distinguish the newly formed shells. In the beginning of September, I procured fifty more of these mussels, and upon opening twelve of them, I found two wherein the young ones seemed to be so perfect, that they would probably soon be excluded from the parent. . . . The unborn mussels being put into a glass tube, and placed before the microscope, I saw with astonishment a most pleasing spectacle, for every one of them, each in its particular membrane had a slow circumvolution, and such turning round or rotatory motion was observable for three hours afterwards. This uncommonly pleasing spectacle was enjoyed by myself, my daughter and the engraver for three whole 165 hours, and we thought it one of the most delightful that could be exhibited.'

He then wrote: 'I took several thousands of these unborn mussels in water, and I saw, beyond my expectations, a great many very little animalcules, of divers sorts and sizes, in this water, a-swimming among the unborn mussels. In these my enquiries, I imagined that the unborn mussels got eaten up by the little animalcules aforesaid; and during my observations, I observed that the fishy matter in the unborn mussels got less from day to day. . . . I have sometimes been puzzled when beholding the multitude of little unborn mussels which lay enclosed in a big mussel; for I was not able to conceive why our canals and fens are not overflowing with mussels. . . . But now, after discovering how the little animals aforesaid devoured them, methought this a sufficient reason why fresh-water mussels are not found in greater plenty.' Dobell (1932) rightly remarks: 'From these observations one can hardly doubt that Leeuwenhoek had got something more than an inkling of the part played by putrefactive micro-organisms in the general economy of nature. To appreciate the novelty of this notion—nowadays commonplace—one must remember that it belongs, historically, to the nineteenth century.'

Leeuwenhoek made an infusion of fresh-water mussels and found many different Ciliates and Flagellates; of these he writes: 'The animalcules had a pretty structure, for the round circumference of their bodies seemed to be made up of ten or twelve brighter round pellets, while in the middle of them there seemed to be a little dark spot, somewhat bigger than the pellets.' Dobell thinks that Leeuwenhoek here was describing Ciliates with food vacuoles, the dark spot being the mega-nucleus; it is likely that Leeuwenhoek also saw the conjugation of Ciliates. He not only described Protozoa in his infusions, but also bacteria such as *Spirillum*: 'little eels, whereof I deemed that eight of them together were no bigger than a blood-corpuscle.' These were the last of his researches on free-living Protozoa and bacteria.

Leeuwenhoek discovers the revivification of rotifers

Although he probably saw Rotifers in the year 1674 the most famous description of them is found in his letter dated February 9th, 1702: 'On the 25th of August (1701) I saw in a leaden gutter, on the front of my house, for a length of about five feet and a breadth of seven inches, some rain-water had remained standing, which had a red colour: and as it occurred to me that this redness might be caused by red animalcules, I took a drop or so of this water and looked at it through a microscope; and I discovered a great many animalcules that were red, and others that were green, whereof the biggest looked no bigger through the microscope than coarse sand does to your naked eye.' Dobell says that the red animalcules were the Phytoflagellate *Haematococcus*, which is very common in gutters. Leeuwenhoek continues: 'On the 31st of August, the water was so far dried up, that if I pressed my finger on the dirt lying on the lead, little more than a drop of water as big as a sand-grain stuck to it. . . . On the 1st of September, the stuff was become so thick that it was like stiff wet clay; but with all my endeavours I could not discover any animalcules in it of the species I had seen before. At length I discovered two living animalcules with oblong bodies, like the largest of those which I had formerly seen in rain-water, wherein pepper or ginger had been infused.' These organisms were Rotifers. 'The matter in the bowels of these creatures was for the most part red, proceeding (as I imagine) from their feeding on smaller animalcules of that colour. . . . The following day the sky was very hot and dry and, about nine in the morning, I took some of the sediment which had been in the leaden gutter, which was then quite dried. . . . This I put into a glass tube, about the thickness of a swan's quill, 167 and poured on it a small quantity of rain-water taken out of my stone cistern, in which water were swimming about some of the animalcules of the afore-mentioned sort (probably these were *Chlamydomonas*). I mixed it up with the dry sediment in order to dissolve the same so that if there were still any living animalcules in it they might issue forth; though I confess I never thought that there could be any living creatures in a substance so dried as this was.

'I was, however, mistaken; for scarce an hour had elapsed, when I saw at least a hundred of the animalcules before described (i.e. rotifers). . . . In the evening I computed there were more than three hundred of the same kind of animalcules, but most of them were not full size, as I judged by their bodies being so minute, and so empty of food, as if they were newly born; and in the bodies of some of the larger ones, I could see two, in others three, young ones folded double. In that part of the animalcules which may be called the breast, I saw a round particle moving with a reciprocal contraction and dilation, in the time one might

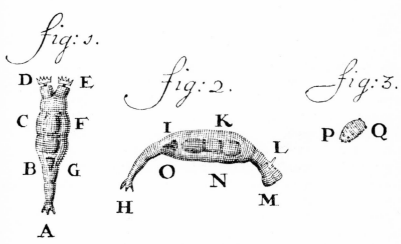

PLATE 21 *Rotifers, revivification from dried stuff in the gutters*

count one: this I did not doubt was the heart' (probably it was the mastax, a structure in the pharynx).

'Moreover, the fore part of the bodies, which may be called the head, was divided into two parts, each of the two divisions being of a round shape set round with certain long and very slender organs, which in their motion exhibited a most pleasing and delightful spectacle; to form an idea of which, we must suppose that we see two small wheels set round the edges with sharp points or pins, and that these wheels are in swift motion from the west towards the south and east, but never move in a contrary direction. . . .

'When one of these animalcules is creeping along the glass, it assumes the figure HIKLMNO (Plate 21, fig. 2): the parts H and M being alternately fixed to the glass, and in this situation the organs like wheels, which in the former figure are shown between D and E, are drawn within the body.' (Earlier, in his letter dated October 17th, 1687, Leeuwenhoek compared this motion with that of a leech or a looper caterpillar.)

He was struck by the 'little wheels' of these animals, but he could not wholly understand them. In the letter of June 28th, 1713, he wrote: 'Furthermore, I paid great attention to their revolving toothed wheel-work; and I saw that an incredible great motion was brought about by the said instrument, in the water round about it, whereby many little particles, that could be made out with the magnifying glass, were wafted towards the animalcule . . . whereof some were used as food by the animalcule. . . . These animalcules, then, and others too, that cannot shift themselves from place to place . . . must be furnished with similar instruments . . . whereby they get any stuff that is in the water for their food and growth and for the defence of their body. . . . I have asked myself: what is the use of such a toothed wheel-work? . . . But if we now let our thoughts run on further, we must decide that such a thing is necessary, if a great stir is to be   169 made in the water . . . this being so, we are faced once more with the mysteries, and inconceivable order . . . with which such tiny creatures are endowed.'

The letter of February 9th, 1702, quoted above, contains a description of the phenomenon of 'revivification' in Rotifers: 'I have often placed the animalcules out of the water, in order to see whether, when all the water about them was evaporated and their bodies exposed to the air, their bodies would burst asunder, as I had often seen in other animalcules. But now I found that when almost all the water was evaporated, so that the creature no longer being covered with water and not able to move itself as usual, then contracted itself into an oval figure, and in that state it remained.

'In order to satisfy myself in this respect, on the third of September, about seven in the morning, I took some of this dry sediment, which I had taken out of the leaden gutter and had stood almost two days in my study, and put a little of it into two separate glass tubes, wherein I poured some rain-water which had been boiled and afterwards cooled. As soon as I had poured on the water, I stirred the whole about and I examined it and perceived some of the animalcules lying closely heaped together. In a short time afterwards they began to extend their bodies, and in about half an hour, at least a hundred of them were swimming about the glass. . . . The preceding experiment I afterwards repeated, and met with the same event. Thus we see that these animalcules, when the water dries away, contract their bodies into an oval shape. . . . We can now easily conceive that in all rain-water which is collected from gutters in cisterns and in all waters exposed to the air, animalcules may be found, for they may be carried thither with the particles of dust blown about by the winds. And not only so, but animalcules, millions of times smaller than a grain of sand, may be carried up in 170 particles of water, if not to the clouds, yet to such a height as to descend with the evening dew: or by the wind they may be raised from the earth, and spread on all sides.

'The preceding kinds of experiments I have repeated many times with the same success, and in particular with some of this sediment which had been kept in my study for above five months. . . . From all these observations, we discern most plainly the incomprehensible perfection, the exact order, and the inscrutable providential care with which the most wise Creator and Lord of the Universe had formed the bodies of these animalcules, which are so minute as to escape our sight, to the end that different species of them may be preserved in existence. And this most wonderful disposition of nature with regard to these animalcules for the preservation of their species; which at the same time strikes us with astonishment, must surely convince all of the absurdity of those old opinions, that living creatures can be produced from corruption or putrefaction.'

Here we see Leeuwenhoek at his best, carrying out careful experiments, often repeated; explaining the distribution of the minute animalcules in their dried state, and using his results to strike at the theory of spontaneous generation. It is true that he did not understand the structure of the 'wheels' (which were explained in 1765 by Bonnet, who said 'they are in truth crowns provided with mobile points'), but their *function* was correctly understood by Leeuwenhoek in 1713.

'Can anyone doubt,' Dobell truly remarks, 'that Leeuwenhoek had, in 1713, discovered the chief function of the peristomial cilia (=wheel-work) of Vorticella? Surely not. Old Antoni knew as well as I do (and everybody else does) how the Vorticellids capture their food from the surrounding water—though he misconceived the structure of the mechanism. By persistent study he had advanced a long way beyond his original interpretations of 1676, and he had at last reached the truth.'

171

CHAPTER EIGHT

Leeuwenhoek
as a Botanist

In many books on the history of botany, Leeuwenhoek is not mentioned. Sachs, in his famous *History of Botany*, 1875, declared: 'Leeuwenhoek's drawings cannot stand a comparison with those of Malpighi or Grew; he did not make his drawings himself, and on the whole his manifold communications give an awkward impression of disruption and dilettantism.' Some other writers have different opinions, however, and I will quote here the words of Professor Dr. G. van Iterson, the Dutch authority on the structure of wood, when writing in 1948 upon Leeuwenhoek's studies on wood: 'I am of the opinion that Leeuwenhoek's drawings and descriptions of the structure of wood, when compared with the figures and accounts published by his contemporaries (Grew and Malpighi), excel by their sober, clear and unprejudiced rendering of what could be discerned microscopically of the finer structure of the examined objects. Grew's drawings of several sorts of wood are much more comprehensive and afford a better survey, but frequently display details that cannot have been observed and must in some cases be relegated to the domain of fantasy. It appears from what Leeuwenhoek tells us about his drawings that he drew the originals and had them copied afterwards. We must own that Leeuwenhoek's descriptions were isolated sketches and that the writer did not know how to give a comprehensive view of

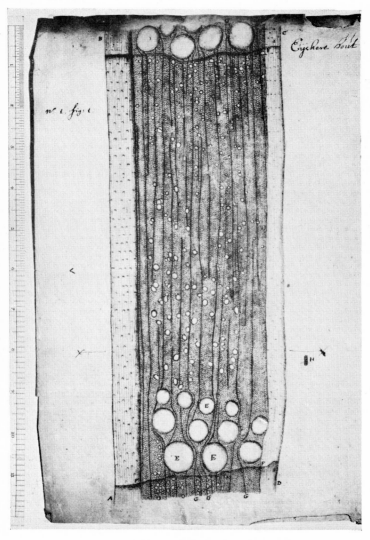

PLATE 22 *Oak-wood drawn by Leeuwenhoek*

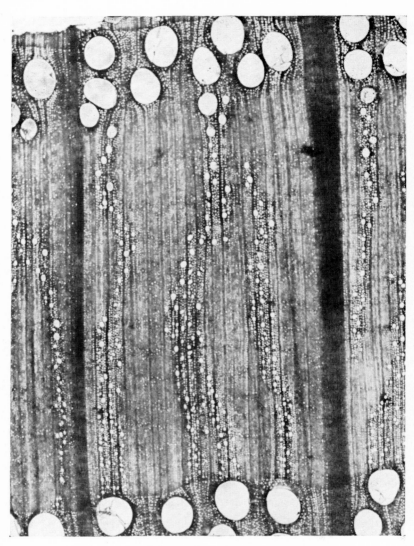

PLATE 23 *Oak-wood, modern photomicrograph*

the structure of plants, as Grew and Malpighi did. . . . Their
books must be considered as attempts at a complete anatomy
of plants. Never had Leeuwenhoek a similar object in view.'
    Van Iterson also said: 'H. C. van Hall (1834) was right
when he stressed the fact that Leeuwenhoek always informs
us consciously when he is at the end of his observations and
adduces suppositions instead of facts, or when he tries to
account for details noticed by him. In this respect he was far
more prudent than his famous contemporaries. It is especially Grew whose descriptions leave the impression that the
supposed structures were realities.' Now Aristotle has
already taught us, 'the facts have not yet been sufficiently
grasped; if ever they are, then credit must be given rather
to observation than to theories, and to theories only if what
they affirm agrees with the observed facts.' Leeuwenhoek
records the facts, and always warns us if he is 'imagining,'
as he calls the formulation of theories.

The structure of wood

It is very difficult to summarize Leeuwenhoek's extensive
and detailed researches on the structure of wood, but it is
interesting to compare, for example, his picture of the
structure of oak with a modern photograph (see Plates 22
and 23).
    In his time it was a common opinion that 'hardwoods' such
as oak, etc., were of better quality if they had been grown
in the north rather than in the south. Leeuwenhoek wrote
that the annual rings were broader in southern wood, and
for that reason he believed it to be better; also, in the case of
conifers (the 'softwoods') he believed that the annual rings
must be small, and his points of view on these matters are
generally accepted today. Leeuwenhoek described for the
first time the wood of a coconut-tree (28th September, 1716,
see Plate 24). He remarked that there were no medullary
rays (thin, vertical plates of cells one to several cells wide,   173

running radially through the tissues of the vascular cylinder), and he was struck by the spirally twisted tracheids, for him a pleasant sight. (A tracheid is a non-living element of the wood, formed from a single elongated cell with tapering ends; the tracheids perform the water-conduction of the plant.) He says, 'Though I had observed this formation of vessels in many other sorts of wood, yet I could not until now

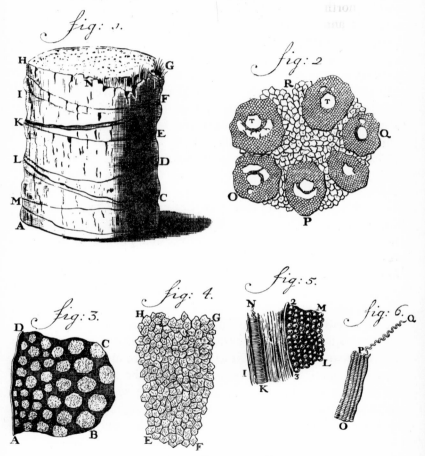

PLATE 24 *Coconut-wood*

venture to say that these vessels were formed in that manner. . . . But now, in this object where the vessel spread out or opened itself a little, I plainly saw the spiral formation, which discovery gave me great pleasure. (Plate 24, fig. 5 N, fig. 6 OPQ.) This circuitous figure of the vessels may be exactly compared to a brass wire, twisted round a small rod. . . . And, when we consider the subject, we cannot, in my humble opinion, conceive any form so suitable for those vessels to raise the juices upwards.' We may suppose that he thought the spiral was a hollow one (not a part of the wall of the cell) and that he compared this 'circuitous vessel' to an Archimedean screw.

In his first letter to the Royal Society, Leeuwenhoek had described mould, in which he saw not only the sporangia (which had previously been discovered by Hooke) but also the formation of the spores (see p. 44).

In another early letter (August 14th, 1675) he said, 'Walking in my garden with a gentleman who is a good botanist, I asked him, pointing to an arum-leaf, what strength there was in it. At the same time, chewing the leaf, I found it caused a sharp stinging in my tongue, which lasted the whole afternoon. I resolved to do my best and discover the cause of the pungency. I found that the leaf consists of particles which I shall call globules, but bear in mind that they are not perfectly round globules. These globules again consisted of particles at least a thousand times smaller. Having pulled the stalk from the leaf, and transversely cut it through, I discovered in the parts of this stalk (which I shall call pores) very thin figures, which lengthwise appeared to me in my microscope, of the thickness of a great bread-knife's back, and its thickness that of a spider's web, when seen by the naked eye. These fine figures lay in the said pores in a heap, some ten or fifteen of them together.'

This was the first description of the 'raphides.' The little needle-shaped crystals, which are formed of calcium oxalate, all lie parallel, enclosed in a mucous substance within the cell, which Leeuwenhoek took for a 'pore.' When the cell is cut open, they slide out and lie in a disordered heap. Leeuwenhoek looked for these needles in other plants and found them in the sap of Vine-branches, Asparagus, White Hellebore (*Veratrum album L.*) and 'Cataputia' (probably *Impatiens noli-me-tangere*). He added, 'in other plants I have not discovered such little pipes,' so we may safely conclude that he examined many more plants.

The stings of nettles

In the case of the raphides, it was an experience in his garden which impelled Leeuwenhoek to make his investigation, and this happened also with his research on the 'stings or prickles of nettles,' which Hooke had described in 1665. Leeuwenhoek wrote (October 17th, 1687), 'At the time I first turned my thoughts to the nature of our common stinging nettles, I imagined that the great pain and swelling of the occasion arose from the sharp points of the stings or prickles, which are thick set on their leaves and stalks, being broken off and left in the skin: but happening one day, while gathering asparagus in my garden, to be stung between my fingers by a very small nettle, it produced so uncommon a pain and swelling, that I examined more narrowly the formation of nettles by the microscope, and I found that the stings or prickles are not only hollow, and contain within them a very transparent juice, but that, at the time when they are in their most vigorous growth, this juice issues from the stings, and may be seen to settle on the points in the shape of a very small drop or globule' (Plate 25, C). He then formed an opinion different from his first, and believed that some acute salt which this liquor contains was responsible for the pain. Hooke thought it was a poison in the prickle, but he did not see the 'round drop or globule': Leeuwenhoek saw it, but failed to realize that this globule was a part of the wall of

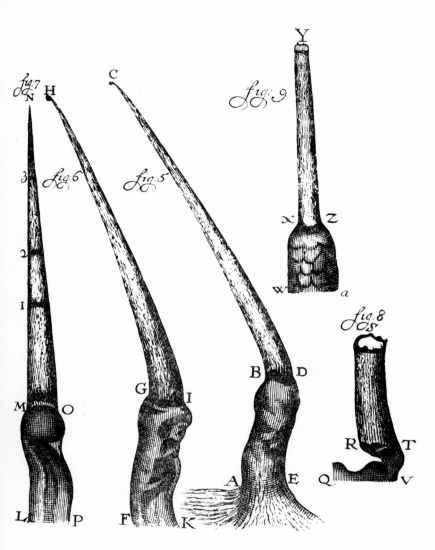

PLATE 25 *Stinging hairs of nettles*

M

the prickle. Thus, as so often happens, our knowledge is pieced together bit by bit!

The transport of substances from cell to cell

Leeuwenhoek also studied the plants from the point of view of a theoretician. He had often seen the globules (=cells) of the plants and he wondered how the water carried the nourishment into these globules (July 13th, 1685). 'I say that all the leaves of trees and plants are formed of globules (besides the vessels or fibres of the leaves), all enclosed in a membrane constituting the surface of the leaf, and the manner in which, I imagine, that these globules, although they touch no vessels, are yet nourished by the vessels, I take to be this: we must first understand, that almost all the leaves of trees and plants while united to the plant, consist

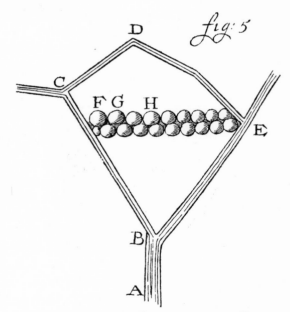

PLATE 26 *Leeuwenhoek's water transport diagram*

of two-thirds parts of water or a watery substance, and that these globules, of which for the greatest part the leaves consist, do not lie singly or separate, but many of them heaped together. Thus let us suppose (see Plate 26) ABCDE to be the vessels . . . then, upon the globule F receiving a supply of nourishment, particularly water, from the vessels to which it is closely conjoined, it must necessarily impart this nourishment to G and from G to H. . . . I have formerly compared this communication of nourishment to dry globules or balls of clay, which we will suppose lying in a glass, and only one of these balls to be made wet, and the moistening being continued, the other balls of clay contiguous to this moist one receive the moisture from it and become wet.' Here, Leeuwenhoek touched upon the difficult problem of transport from cell to cell—still a puzzle today! In the textbooks of botany one reads 'the transfer of water between the cells is facilitated by the occurrence of thin areas, or *pits*,' but this description does not solve the problem!

Leeuwenhoek saw these pits quite clearly, as we see from his letter of August 12th, 1692. Huygens had asked him about the structure of a 'pipe in the wood,' and Leeuwenhoek described pine-wood with its tracheids and 'bordered pits.' He said that at first he had taken them for 'globules,' but then he saw that they possessed little round apertures. He saw the spiral thickening of the walls of the tracheids, and thought that there was a little spirally twisted 'pipe' around the greater pipe; he began to imagine that such spirally twisted pipes were one of the most common structures in the organic world. Since he saw the bordered pits only in places where the 'ascending pipes' joined the 'horizontal ones' (i.e., the medullary rays), he thought that the pits might serve to give water and nourishment to these horizontal pipes. He therefore examined the structure of rushes, and discovered what he described as 'great vessels,' now known as the *aerenchyma*, a tissue with large intercellular spaces, for transporting

179

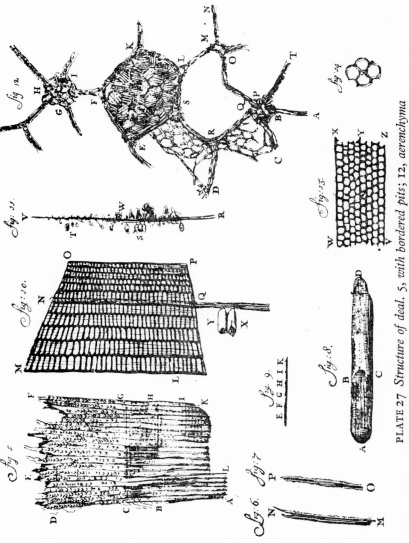

PLATE 27 *Structure of deal. 5, with bordered pits; 12, aerenchyma*

oxygen to the submerged parts of aquatic plants such as the rush. (Plate 27.)

The development of seeds

As already mentioned in the chapter on spermatozoa, Leeuwenhoek thought that the embryo was in the 'seed' of the man. No wonder, therefore, that he was very interested in the seeds of plants and the embryos they contained: he germinated many seeds in his study, and described their progress. For instance, he examined the seed of the willow (July 13th, 1685): 'In order further to satisfy my curiosity respecting this very minute seed, from which so large a tree as the willow is produced, I took some of the seeds and, in the month of June, placed them in moist sand in my closet, in order to see how the beginning of vegetation would be performed in this very small seed. But before I put the seed into the sand, and while it was yet very dry, I viewed it with the microscope. . . .' He gave a drawing to show the part of the seed from which the root would arise, and after it had been in the damp sand for thirty-six hours, he examined it again, finding that this part had increased in length and put out no less than six little roots. As the Dutch botanist Dr. Karstens remarks, van Tieghem claimed these discoveries, but Leeuwenhoek had made them two centuries earlier!

A most remarkable description, in my opinion, is to be found in the letter dated August 24th, 1688. 'Among many other seeds I have particularly examined the grains of wheat; and in them the young plant I have mentioned, before it began to vegetate, having first either put them in water for a short time, or held a few grains in my mouth, merely to moisten the outward membranes, whereby they could be easier taken off. . . . I many times endeavoured to trace in the young plant, while in the seed, the vestige or first formation of the ear, but all my endeavours, even with the assistance of my microscopes, were fruitless. . . . Then I took a   181

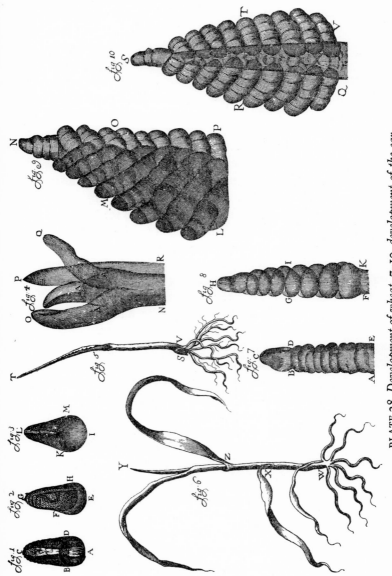

PLATE 28 *Development of wheat. 7–10, development of the ear*

small brass box, almost filled with sand, and I moistened the sand with rain-water. . . . At the end of four days, I took out the middle part of the plant, wherein by the help of the microscope I perceived some minute leaves, and, from their appearance, I was well assured that the ear between them had increased in size, though I could not distinctly perceive it.' (Plate 28.) 'After carrying the box and the remaining grains in my pocket four days longer, I opened it again and, taking out from one of the shoots that part which contained the innermost leaf immediately enclosing the ear, I placed it before the microscope, directing the limner to make a drawing of it. This is shown in Plate 28, fig. 1, ABCD, where ABD is the young ear and BCD the inner leaf enclosing it. At the end of four days more, being the twelfth day, I opened another grain, and having separated the young leaves a little asunder, I was much more confident than before, that I discerned the ear; this I also caused to be drawn from the microscope as in fig. 2, EFGH.

'From these observations we may be fully assured, that warmth and water will, of themselves alone, promote the growth of plants. And also, that God, the all-wise Creator of the Universe, does not create any new species of things on this earth, but that, at the beginning, He so ordained and constituted all things that, his Creation being perfect, the seeds of plants, when come to maturity, shall produce or contain in themselves (however undiscoverable by us) the part or vegetative principle of the future plant, which in its due time will be produced, and that in all respects conformable to the original plant. And this I take to be a certain truth, which prevails not only in plants, but in all living creatures whatsoever.'

Leeuwenhoek went on with these observations and was able to cut open a wheat-plant, sown in the preceding autumn, which in April had grown to the size shown in fig. 6. After taking away the leaves, he viewed the ear (fig. 7), 183 and on May 12th and May 17th he continued his observations (figs. 8, 9 and 10). He was a convinced preformationist, and he could found his theories on facts, for he imagined that the embryo in the seed was the first rudiment of the new plant, and here he saw the leaves, the roots and the ear!

Salts in plants

Leeuwenhoek gave much attention to 'salts' or crystals in the plants he examined. He discovered (November 28th, 1687) the fibres in the bark of 'China-China' or *Cinchona*, the tree from which quinine is extracted. During his examination of the bark, he discovered a colour-reaction, which was re-discovered in 1858 by Grahe at Kasan, and is now called Grahe's test. Professor P. van der Wielen writes: 'Part of the observations on *Cinchona* which Leeuwenhoek described is to be found again in the latest issue of the Dutch Pharmacopoeia, "If a piece of *Cinchona* is heated in a test tube, a crimson tar is deposited in it." Leeuwenhoek's description of the colour is, however, much more accurate: "I have then put the said bark near such a powerful fire that it quite burnt to charcoal, and I have gathered or caught all the oil and fluid with the exception of very little. This oil had a beautiful purple colour." '

Another example of his experimental researches is that on the salts of 'Pareira brava' (*Cissampelos pareira* L. or *Chondodendrum tomentosum* R.P.), whose medicinal virtues were described in the *Philosophical Transactions*. He extracted the salts: 'then, because I imagined that these particles were no other than absolute salts, I immersed some of them in burnt wine, but all of them preserved their shapes.' He then took a new extract, and 'put a drop of it and mixed it with some blood, which I drew from my finger. Whereupon I saw that the globules of the blood from whence its redness proceeds, were more separated. . . . There was also this remarkable appearance, that most of the globules had a kind of sinus or

184

cavity in them. And when the globules, after assuming a flat shape, got somewhat closer together, they put on an oval figure. When the globules of the blood are concreted or coagulated, they exhibit the appearance of a solid body.' He also placed the cells with starch grains of the root which he called the 'mealy ones' over a burning coal, and 'now they assumed a flat shape of a circular figure.'

'Let us now suppose these very minute particles, which I call mealy ones, to be administered as a medicine, and by the heat and moisture of the body to be dissolved: let us further to suppose that these dissolved particles are, by the continual motion and agitation of the body, comminuted and broken into other particles of inconceivable tenuity and fineness. We do indeed hereby gain some insight into the manner of nature's operation of healing; but in what particular manner the particles, so attenuated, do act in the accomplishment of their purpose will, if I mistake not, for ever remain undiscoverable by human power.' This he wrote in the later part of his life (October 8th, 1717).

Among Leeuwenhoek's other botanical observations were some on the type of hairs found in the family Labiatae, and the vesicles (=cells) with lupuline* in hop. He carefully studied starch grains (March 26th, 1675, and later), comparing cooked grains with those found in the dung of pigeons and sparrows.

He wrote on botanical subjects in eighty of his letters, and he made so many discoveries that the great botanist Robert Brown was inspired to name a genus *Levenhookia*† after him! Treviranus characterised the microscopists of this time: 'Hooke gives only a few figures, but they are serviceable; Grew is the most graceful, Malpighi the most detailed, Leeuwenhoek the most faithful. Malpighi and Grew were often carried away by their preconceived opinions, but their works

---

* Lupuline is a resinous excretion of the hop-plant.
† *Levenhookia* is an Australian genus of the Stylididae.

were systematic; Leeuwenhoek only gives detached notes, but rich contributions, up to the present often undervalued, to the anatomy of plants.' The examples of his researches which have been mentioned in this chapter suggest that the words of Treviranus, written more than a century ago, are still true today!

CHAPTER NINE

Leeuwenhoek and Medicine: the Study of Crystals, Chemistry, Physics and Ecology

Like many others in his time, Leeuwenhoek did not confine himself to one science; he also tackled many subjects other than microbiology, and in this chapter we shall attempt to give an impression of his relation to some of the sciences mentioned above.

Medical science

Though Leeuwenhoek was a matter-of-fact man, who relied on his own judgement, he was full of self-criticism; he was also a critic of others who, according to him, were at fault. This is evident from his attitude towards the medical science of his time. In a letter written in 1699, he stated that a certain doctor had administered a powder to 'a woman suffering from some moist substances oozing from one of her legs.' This powder had caused eight movements of her bowels, and she had also developed pimples all over her body. Leeuwenhoek explained this in his own way by assuming that the blood had thickened so much that it was unable to circulate in the skin, and so had caused the pimples to develop. 'Hearing of this ill-treatment of strong purging, and also that her body had broken out in red pimples, I burst out violently, saying: the administering to so weak a human body of a powder of such violent effects, might sooner be called a treatment to murder than to cure a patient.' We must suppose that the doctor did not appreciate this outburst very much, especially as it was made known all over the world in Leeuwenhoek's writings, without, however, mentioning the physician's name. A powder which could have such an effect when only 1/10,240 of a pound was administered, was a murderous remedy in Leeuwenhoek's eyes; it was not only Molière who mobilised mankind against the purgers!

In his letter of April 5th, 1697, Leeuwenhoek attacked a German quack, who claimed wonders for his 'powder sympathy,' saying that it could crush a stone in the body of a human and cure severe festering. Leeuwenhoek first let the man have his say, and then asked him to be allowed to explain his feelings about this powder, being a Dutchman not given to flattery. In the first place, he asked him how he had got rid of the pus in the ulcer, to which the quack replied that he had drained it off by the urine. Leeuwenhoek said that this was impossible, the pus being much too thick to pass through such narrow blood-vessels. The answer, that there are more things than this which we cannot explain, did not satisfy him. As for the crushing of the stone, Leeuwenhoek did not accept this and said flatly: 'Those who boast that they can either crush the stone in the bladder or the kidneys or drain it off, are but impostors.'

In his letter of March 2nd, 1694, he described a so-called cure for hardness of hearing. 'A very aged man came to me, telling me that for some time he had been hard of hearing, but he added, a famous doctor living in the country had quite cured him.' Leeuwenhoek coolly suggested that probably his hardness of hearing had been caused only by a plug of dirt in the external ear passage, whereupon the man told him that an incredible amount of thick yellowish matter had come out of his ears! Leeuwenhoek did not like such practices and therefore he devoted a letter to the subject of ear-wax and he advised people to use an ear-pick. He did not attach any belief to the stories told by quacks, nor was he deceived by the tales of patients who often succeeded in making their doctors believe them.

'Some years ago a doctor came to me and showed me a piece of paper on which were some small particles. According to this physician, a woman had passed them with her urine.' Leeuwenhoek examined the particles and recognised them as being the seeds of red-currants. To the question how they had come to be in the urine, Leeuwenhoek answered that he did not believe that they had been in the urine at all. He rather believed that one of the servant girls had put them in her mistress's chamber pot, the better to be able to pity her (letter April 22nd, 1692). As if this answer was not yet plain enough, he continued: 'In our town we have an example of a certain female who makes simple people believe that in passing water she gets rid of several stones, from which she suffers much. A doctor and also some of the clergy believed her, hence many people had great pity on her and this made quite a stir in the town. This doctor handed me such a stone to examine. But I instantly returned it after striking it with a key, and seeing with the naked eye that it was a piece of flagstone.' This was also borne out by some professors to whom he had shown the stone; evidently his simple method of showing up the deceit had to be corroborated by the academic methods of professors! Although Leeuwenhoek's opinions were *mechanistic*, as mentioned in Chapter Three, they were quite in accord with those held by most people of his time, as chemistry was then still in its infancy. These views are perhaps most apparent from his statement in the letter of April 22nd, 1692: 'So now I have refuted the argument of many doctors and surgeons, who, when they do not know the real cause of an illness, say: the blood has started to ferment, etc. As for me, I am more certain now than before, that every movement of the blood   189 depends upon the heart, and it would be better to say the blood is too thick, it cannot be driven through the narrow vessels and hence it cannot circulate. Now when the blood has become so much thicker that it cannot pass through and the vessels are consequently blocked up, it is my opinion that if the heart is still so strong as to drive the blood through, red spots will appear in the skin.' Cold, too, would congeal the blood, as Leeuwenhoek saw in the bat.

In this way he explained smallpox, and for the same reason he always drank as much tea and coffee as he could, and that as hot as possible, thinking to dilute the blood and so expel the noxious and harmful matters. When he felt a fever coming on, or when his urine had a reddish colour, when a man had a bad leg or an ulcer, when he was consulted about gall, kidney or bladder stones, or when he had a headache (which he thought was caused by the fact that the blood could not get through to the brain fast enough), his advice was always the same: drink much, preferably hot tea or coffee. The physician Bontekoe had advocated this cure, and in this he was ardently followed by Leeuwenhoek, who was perhaps strengthened in his opinions by the fact that he had seen the capillaries and noted their small size.

Crystals

When Leeuwenhoek was considering crystals, he did not then conceive of the globule as being the smallest element; as early as 1675, in his letter dated August 14th, he expressed his opinion that every crystal, however small, retains the same form and shape as a large one, so that a large crystal may be thought of as a stack of such small crystals. Similar pronouncements are to be found in the letters of January 23rd, 1679; November 14th, 1679; and January 5th, 1685.

The Dutch scientist, Professor Dr. R. Hooykaas, who has made a close study of the early history of crystallography,

190

says that in principle there are two theories about the structure of crystals: (1) Crystals are built up by stacking polyhedric elementary crystals onto the faces of a nuclear crystal, a view still held by modern crystallographers (modern theory maintains that the atoms in crystals are arranged in regular patterns formed by the angles of parallelepipeds or cubes).

(2) Crystals are built up by stacking globular or ellipsoidal elementary crystals.

He adds (1950): 'Without hesitation we can consider A. van Leeuwenhoek to be the founder of the theory that crystals are formed by the conjunction of elementary crystal-molecules having the same shape as the larger crystals.'

Chemistry and physics

In the preceding chapters little has been said about Leeuwenhoek's investigations in the field of chemistry and physics. He knew, however, how to separate gold and silver from their ores, and he could inform the East India Company that the so-called 'Gold-ore' from Sumatra contained a sulphide instead of gold (letter dated February 14th, 1699). He saw that the crystals which he obtained by putting the so-called 'Crab-eyes' or Crab-stones* and the claws of lobsters into vinegar, were identical in form (they are in fact crystals of calcium acetate). This is an example of a microchemical reaction in which the final product is recognized by its crystalline form (compare the reaction given by *Cinchona* bark, Chapter Eight).

Leeuwenhoek measured the volume of gas formed when gunpowder was burnt, and he arrived at the figure of 2080:1, a value quite close to those obtained by other investigators of his time (e.g. values of 2276:1 and 2200:1). He also experimented with lodestones and constructed a little air-pump.

* These are the chalky deposits in the stomach of certain crabs. They are stores of calcium needed in the process of calcification of the exoskeleton after moulting and they were used in Leeuwenhoek's time as a source of therapeutic chalk.

In his early years he thought that there was a 'fire-element,' but in his letter dated September 28th, 1716, he spoke of 'the motion, which we call heat'; it is possible that he obtained this idea from Hooke or from Christiaan Huygens.

Ecology: the struggle for life

At the present time, ecology has assumed a very great importance in the study of biology, and it is interesting to study Leeuwenhoek's thoughts on this subject which are scattered throughout his works. He was aware of the struggle for existence, and he associated this with the great number of the spermatozoa; just as a tree has numberless seeds, of which only a small number will give rise to new trees, and just as, of many pips planted in a single hole, only one will develop, so it is with the spermatozoa. The reason for this overproduction is the concern of the omniscient Creator; we can only make out the *nature* of things, not their *reason* for being so.

We have already discussed Leeuwenhoek's ideas on the distribution of the micro-organisms in connection with his discovery of the dried-up Rotifers and the encapsulated Protozoa. These views may be summarized in the following quotation from his letter of April 28th, 1702: 'We may, therefore, conclude that in all pools and marshes, which have water standing in them in winter, but dry up in summer, many kinds of animalcules ought to be found; and even though there were none at first in such water, they would be brought thither by water-fowl, by way of the mud or water sticking to their feet and feathers.'

He discovered the plankton in the sea, in fresh water, and the micro-organisms in the soil.

'If we were asked to what end such small creatures have been created, the only answer we could think of would be this: cod, ling, etc., eat not only haddock, but also small fish, 192 haddock again eat whiting, whiting eat small fish among which are shrimps, and shrimps again eat smaller fish, in short one species is created to serve as food for another.'

He also realized that animals like the Copepod crustacean *Cyclops* (which he discovered on October 16th, 1699) have an important position in food chains, and that herring, in whose stomachs no food is ever found, feed on microscopic animals and plants and on eggs; he also knew that bacteria form the last link in the chain, so that from his writings we gain a representation of a complete food chain.

While investigating the aphids, he found that they were adapted to only one species of plant, and so he noticed the phenomenon of the 'ecological niche.' Leeuwenhoek also noticed that the larger animals have fewer young than the smaller animals, and so they occur in fewer numbers than the smaller animals which form their food; this makes us think that he was aware of the principle of the so-called 'food-pyramid.' He was also certain that the small sessile animals such as *Vorticella* wave the minute particles of food towards their mouth, and so he established this first link in the food chain. He did not know that plants are able to assimilate carbon dioxide (photosynthesis), so he was unable to trace the chain to its ultimate end. If Leeuwenhoek had collected his ecological views into a single unified whole, they would have certainly attracted much attention; as they are only to be found in occasional letters, it seems that they passed unnoticed.

N

CHAPTER TEN

Leeuwenhoek,
Immortal Scientist

In the preceding chapters we have tried to show Leeuwenhoek's achievements in various departments of science, and as far as possible we have let his own words reveal his methods of working and of reasoning. It is obvious that he often wrestled for a long time with the problems that occupied his mind, and in some cases it was only after many years that he succeeded in finding a solution that satisfied him. As A. W. Meyer (*Osiris,* 1937) has shown, he tackled his problems experimentally. Often he showed unusual shrewdness, and this caused his contemporaries to remark that his mind was sharper than his sharpest glasses; his perfect honesty made him communicate his mistakes and errors to the reader (even when he had corrected them himself), and this may easily confuse a superficial student of his works. Also the habit of dealing with several different subjects in the same letter will no doubt have assisted in creating the impression that Leeuwenhoek was a man of 'mediocre mind, but with marvellous hands; a pair of hands directed by other minds.'

In order to obtain a true impression of Leeuwenhoek's investigations, it is necessary to collect systematically the writings on the various topics from his letters, and in the earlier chapters this has been done for several subjects.

Dobell set an example in his authoritative work *Leeuwenhoek and His Little Animals* (1932), whilst Cole (1937) did so for several other topics in the zoological field. It is only when this method is followed that Leeuwenhoek's real greatness becomes apparent.

It can be seen from the foregoing chapters that Leeuwenhoek undoubtedly deserves the name of 'the father of microbiology'; he acquired great merit as a histologist, and he did extremely valuable work as a botanist. He also advanced the study of both pure and applied entomology, and discovered not only spermatozoa, but also parthenogenesis, and the asexual propagation by means of budding; in addition to all this, he also set up a new theory of generation, and discovered numerous organisms. All these discoveries are scattered throughout his writings and are nowhere systematically displayed. We might blame him for not doing this, unless we remember that he knew Hooke's *Micrographia* only from its figures, and the *Philosophical Transactions* naturally contain the most heterogeneous collection of subjects.

With Hooke, as well as with Leeuwenhoek, the microscope formed the connecting link; everything which he could investigate with his own glasses and methods he examined, just as today with the first publications describing research with the electron microscope. Moreover, we should not forget that in one of his first letters, Leeuwenhoek complained that at Delft there was no one with whom he could discuss his work, which is why he asked the Royal Society not only to suggest subjects for his research, but also to criticize it. On the whole, however, Leeuwenhoek went his own way, despite the authorities of his time. In his first writings he corrected some of the observations made by Hooke, and later he disagreed with Swammerdam, de Graaf, Harvey, Descartes and others. With the most perfect coolness he declared: 'If Mr Vallisneri is against my theses, there are thousands who are for them; in our country we have a proverb saying, "One woodcock does not make a

cold winter".' When the Royal Society doubted his discovery
of the animalcules, he persisted in his views, and in the end
triumphed. Again, when a number of medical men disagreed
with him, he remarked that doctors must often conjecture,
and that he had a right to his opinion as they had to theirs
(September 12th, 1696). The story that Leeuwenhoek's
hands were directed by brains in London ought to be con-
demned as quickly as it originated.

Spontaneous generation

Leeuwenhoek was driven by a passionate desire to penetrate
more deeply into the mysteries of creation. To him, as to
many others of his time, a watch was a greater specimen of
craftsmanship than a clock in a tower; this opinion is reflected
in his biological views. The microscope gave him the opportunity to study and admire the small organisms, the 'animalcules,' and whenever he was able he expressed his admiration
of all the beautiful things he saw. As a consequence he did
not believe that such marvellously-built organisms arose from
putrefaction and he expressed his feelings on this in the
following words: 'A flea or a louse can no more come into
being from a little bit of dirt than a horse from a dunghill.'
It seems that this is the principal reason for his rejection of
the theory of spontaneous generation. As living and moving
were one and the same to him, it is obvious that he thought
the rudiments of developing organisms to be present in the
fast-moving spermatozoa which he discovered. He spared no
pains to find them in the semen of many kinds of different
animals, and in this way he became the founder of the school
of 'animalculists.'

Leeuwenhoek's general theories

From this it is evident that he had certain general theories,
such as his idea that all animals were built in more or
196   less the same way. This theory (still held by many famous

biologists a century after Leeuwenhoek's death) often put him on the wrong track, but it was, nevertheless, an incentive to his researches. At the beginning of his work he thought that all organic matter (and also much of the inorganic) was formed of globules, but he did not adhere tenaciously to this opinion. When a closer investigation taught him that dentine and muscles, for example, were built up from other elements, he frankly admitted his error. In later life he was struck with the common occurrence of a spiral structure, and he then thought that he had found a very general structural principle; in several of his writings he puts forward an opinion which is very similar to Goethe's 'Spiraltendenz.' Leeuwenhoek did not confine himself to the vegetable kingdom: *Spirogyra*, the stalk of *Vorticella*, tracheids in plants, tracheae of insects, muscle fibres and tendons of various animals all presented, according to him, the same structure.

Applied science

Leeuwenhoek very often drew practical conclusions from his fundamental researches, so moving into the field of applied science. In Chapter Nine we have drawn attention to his theory that the blood must be kept thin, if it is to flow through the narrow capillaries. In the chapter on entomology we have stressed several times the attention which Leeuwenhoek paid to the fight against the insects which he studied so carefully; for instance, he attached special importance to the mites, which he thought acted as scavengers, and so were important as a species which keeps another one in check.

The place of Leeuwenhoek in his time

One of the questions that forces itself upon us is: 'What position does Leeuwenhoek hold in the history of science?' In order to attempt an answer to this question, it is first necessary to say something about the general trend of science at that time. The renascence of science started as early as the 197 sixteenth century, but did not come to full development until the early part of the seventeenth century. It was in the south of Europe particularly that the new ideas broke ground; there, it was Galileo who experimented and dared to attack the traditional science. The man who discovered the circulation of the blood, William Harvey, was educated in Italy, and many like him could be mentioned.

In England, Francis Bacon in his *Advancement of Learning* (1605) proclaimed that empiricism (true observation, and the drawing of conclusions from a series of facts) would bring about the advancement of knowledge. Some years later, in 1620, he published his *Novum Organum*, on the title page of which is shown a ship in full sail, confidently sailing to the unknown seas beyond the Pillars of Hercules, leaving Antiquity behind it. The saying 'Scientia est potentia' (knowledge is power) is due to Francis Bacon, and he thought that by understanding the laws of nature one would be able to control it, so laying the foundations of technology. Although Bacon is often called 'the herald of modern times,' his ideas had often been put into practice before; 'journeys of exploration,' in which the old world was left and the new one was discovered, had been going on for more than a century. It would be wrong to disparage Bacon's work on account of this; rather it gave a philosophical basis to the new thought.

In the seventeenth century more was happening that was of the greatest consequence for the development of science. Whereas the old universities had been established by the State and the Church in order to educate students of law and medicine, and the priests, and to qualify them for their professions, in the seventeenth century a number of persons in various places formed 'societies' or 'academies' outside the universities. Among the first of these societies were those in Italy; Francis Bacon, too, had dreamt of such societies in his 'New Atlantis.' Soon, such companies also arose in the north; one of the most important was undoubtedly the Royal

Society, which had been started as an informal group in 1645, but was put on a firm footing by the Royal Charter of 1662. In this fashion science was secularized.

These societies, as Bacon had foreseen, became the centres of scientific research, whereas the universities often remained very conservative. The periodicals which were published by the societies (such as the *Philosophical Transactions* of the Royal Society, and the *Journal des Sçavans* of the Paris Academy, both started in 1665) provided the research workers with an opportunity of publishing the results of their work, and these writings often acted as an incentive to others.

Whereas formerly only a few instruments were known, many new ones were added in the seventeenth century, among them the microscope (see Chapter Two). It might be thought that this precious new instrument would at once attract attention, but it did not do so until 1665, when Robert Hooke, Curator to the Royal Society, published his *Micrographia*.

How does Leeuwenhoek fit into this development? It is clear that he did not invent the microscope, despite frequent statements to the contrary, and it is obvious, too, that he, the simple usher of the Delft magistrates, was in no way connected with a university. Because he had passed an examination as a land surveyor, he was appointed 'wijn-roeyer' or 'gauger' of Delft. As such, he had to inspect weights and measures, hence measuring became second nature to him; it was in fact one of his most remarkable characteristics. Galileo had set science the task of measuring as much as was possible, and Leeuwenhoek was the first to carry this out with respect to microscopic objects. As he constructed a microscope of his own with only one lens, he had a certain advantage, as the compound microscope of his day gave a wrong impression of the object because the faults of the lenses were cumulative and introduced errors.

Reinier de Graaf, the doctor of medicine living in Delft,   199 himself a great research worker unconnected with a university, introduced Leeuwenhoek to the Royal Society (in April, 1673). In this way, Leeuwenhoek came into contact with a number of scientists who were all enthusiastic about the principles of Francis Bacon; they respected facts and hoped to develop science in an inductive fashion. Science thus became secularized, but this must not be thought of as meaning irreligious; on the contrary, Leeuwenhoek thought that the microscopic organisms were greater marvels than the macroscopic ones. His works are full of his admiration of creation and the Creator, a theme which is frequently found in writings of this period; in becoming better acquainted with creation, men wanted to get nearer the Creator, a conviction which is found among many of the early members of the Royal Society.

Among the factors involved in the renascence of science which were to Leeuwenhoek's advantage were the establishment—outside of the universities—of 'Societies' and 'Academies' controlling the study of various sciences; the fact that the Royal Society published a periodical in which Leeuwenhoek's communications (though often abridged) were inserted; and the mathematical trend started by Galileo, with which Leeuwenhoek felt much at home. Also very important were Leeuwenhoek's detached observations and experiments, suiting the spirit of the times, and his inclination to put his discoveries into practice if at all possible, and the empirical trend brought so much to the fore by Francis Bacon. Perhaps most important of all, however, was Leeuwenhoek's microscope, which he had modified in such a way that it undoubtedly surpassed all existing instruments. All of these factors serve to show that whereas formerly people had had a somewhat romantic outlook on nature, in which mysticism often played a part, in the seventeenth century people became more matter-of-fact, and Leeuwenhoek in particular was very much of this type. Again, Delft was a small town where everyone knew everyone else, so it is no wonder that Leeuwenhoek's intelligence drew the attention of the magistrates and of physicians such as Reinier de Graaf. It thus seems that all the necessary conditions were present for Leeuwenhoek to act and attract attention, but this does not in itself provide a sufficient explanation of his success. There is no getting away from the fact that men of genius are oddities, who are often beyond explanation; it is also a fact that a genius must also fit in with the attitude of mind of his own times in order that he shall find acceptance. Even a genius does not get things thrown into his lap and, day in, day out, Leeuwenhoek was busy with his problems from which he could never escape. He was incredibly honest, frankly admitting his errors and always willing to reconsider a wrong opinion if facts, observation or experiment showed him that his former hypothesis was not correct. Leeuwenhoek rigidly kept his observations separate from his speculations (or 'imaginings'), and he continually returned to problems, even if he thought that they had been correctly solved. It was in this way that he became the man of whom the Dutch are so proud. As Sarton has said, 'Facts can only be explained by theories, but they can never be explained away, thus, however insignificant in themselves, they remain supreme.' Leeuwenhoek discovered a multitude of facts, and tried to explain them by theories which he was always ready to modify if they did not match the facts.

Leeuwenhoek's influence in his own time and later

Leeuwenhoek's house at Delft was very often visited by learned men, kings and other important people, who were eager to see the wonders of the world of microscopic objects. A second edition of his letters published in Dutch was widely read, as can be judged from the fact that an old lady at Batavia (now Djakarta), having read his works, sent him a trunk of the coconut-palm. Through the publication of his letters in the *Philosophical Transactions* they reached a large public, so that we may assume that his influence in his own time was very great.

Linnaeus came soon after Leeuwenhoek, and then the systematic trend became important in biology so that Leeuwenhoek's influence declined; probably also there was a feeling that nearly everything had now been discovered in microscopy, which was now no more than a pleasant entertainment for idle hours. This is apparent from the titles of books published soon after Leeuwenhoek's death. H. Baker called his work *The Microscope Made Easy* (1742), Ledermüller's book was entitled *Mikroskopische Augen-und Gemüths-Ergötzung* (*Microscopical Amusements for Eyes and Mind*) (1760, 1765). J. Baster also spoke of *Natuurkundige uitspanningen* (1759) i.e. Diversions in physics.

It may be regretted that Leeuwenhoek did not train any pupils, but he himself gave the following reason for this in a letter to Leibnitz (September 28th, 1715): 'I don't see that much use would result from establishing a school for the training of young people to grind lenses. Besides, it is my firm conviction that of a thousand people there is not one capable of applying himself to such a study, for it requires much time and the expenditure of much money. Also one's mind ought constantly to be busy if one wants to accomplish anything. Moreover, most people are not of an enquiring mind, nay, some of whom one would never have expected it say: "What is the use whether we know or not?" '

Leeuwenhoek himself possessed the qualities of an investigator to a very large degree, and the pioneering work which he performed deserves our attention even today. He could measure a large part of the world of microscopic objects, most of which had never been seen before his time. He once said (April 30th, 1698): 'Through labour and diligence we can discover matters which we had thought inscrutable before.' In this he was undoubtedly right, but we must not forget that his own keen intelligence played a large part in his work. It was his ardent desire to learn the truth, his enormous devotion to his work and his unremitting study throughout many years that gained for him his splendid results. He made mistakes, of course, but what research worker does not make them? What pioneer produces results that last for all time? Leeuwenhoek is certainly one of the greatest naturalists that the world has ever known, and he justly deserves the title: *Leeuwenhoek—Immortal Scientist!*

The compilation of a complete bibliography of Leeuwenhoek's printed letters is a most difficult task; the most comprehensive is that of F. J. Cole (Annals of Science, Vol. 2, April 1937) entitled 'Leeuwenhoek's Zoological Researches Part II, Bibliography and analytical index.' In this article Cole gives in tabular form the following information:

1. The number of the letter
2. Date
3. Age of Leeuwenhoek at that time
4. Information on the first Dutch edition
5. Information on the first Latin edition
6. The reference to the letter's place in the Philosophical Transactions
7. The reference to the letter's place in Hoole's 'Select Works of Antoni van Leeuwenhoek' (1798, 1807)
8. The year of the first publication

In the analytical index, Cole also gives references to the letters which mention particular animals and structures.

It was Dobell who said that until the *complete* writings of Leeuwenhoek could be studied in their original state and sequence, it would be impossible to form a just estimate of the extent and value of his scientific discoveries; I would agree with this, but I would also agree with Cole who held that strict adherence to this would postpone to the dim and distant future any further pronouncement on Leeuwenhoek's researches.

The 'Collected Letters of Antoni van Leeuwenhoek,' of which I have the honour of being the editor-in-chief, will not be complete for a number of years; many scientists have contributed to this work, and I am sure that in the year 2000 we shall have a much better understanding of Leeuwenhoek than we have today.

Dobell, in his classic book published in 1932 ('A. van Leeuwenhoek and his little animals'), has given an elaborate list of the chief printed versions of the letters, both in Dutch and in Latin; he points out, as P. Harting also did in 1875, that the letters generally made their appearance a few at a time, in the form of a brochure with a common title. These brochures were often issued by different publishers, and the final 'complete' collections were made up of these earlier partial collections of various editions and issues. For example, the Dutch editions begin with letter 28 (April 25th, 1679), but letters 32, 33, and 39 (dated June 14th, 1684, November 12th, 1680, and September 12 (in mistake for the 17th) 1683 respectively) were published first with an introduction by the publisher Daniel van Gaesbeeck of Leyden in which he says that Leeuwenhoek himself did not give him the manuscript. As Dobell says, perfect copies, composed of first editions throughout, complete with all the plates, are now extremely rare. He had only seen one—his own—whilst Cole did not have a complete set of first editions. As I am in possession of such a set I will give a description of it.

Dutch Edition

Volume 1

Title-plate   Ontdeckte onsigtbaarheeden, 1685 by R. de Hooghe.

Title-page   Ontledingen en Ontdekkingen, Boutesteyn 1686. Leyden.

Letters 28, 29, 30, 31, 34, 35, 36 (Dobell no. 8).

Title-page   Boutesteyn 1685. Leyden.
Letters 38, 42, 43 (Dobell no. 5).

Title-page   Boutesteyn 1685. Leyden.
Letters 46, 47 (Dobell no. 7).

Title-page   Boutesteyn 1685. Leyden.
Letters 44, 45 (Dobell no. 6).

Title-page   Boutesteyn 1686. Leyden.
Letters 48, 49, 50, 51, 52 (Dobell no. 9).

Title-page   Boutesteyn 1687. Leyden. Vervolg der Brieven (Dobell no. 10).

Letters 53–60 (April 4th, 1687–November 28th, 1687), pp. 155. With a list of Leeuwenhoek's letters 28–52 and their contents.

Title-page   van Gaesbeeck. Leyden 1684. Ondervindingen en Beschouwingen.

Letters 32, 33, 39 (Dobell thought that letter 39 was published with no. 37, but he has written to me to say that he now agrees with my opinion that no. 39 was published with 32 and 33 in the first brochure. Dobell no. 1).

Title-page   van Gaesbeeck, Leyden 1684 (Dobell no. 2).
Letter 37 (January 22nd, 1683).

Title-page   van Gaesbeeck, Leyden 1684 (Dobell no. 4).
Letter 41 (April 14th, 1684).

Title-page   van Gaesbeeck, Leyden 1684 (Dobell no. 3).
Letter 40 (December 28th, 1683).

Volume 2

Portrait

Title-page   Vervolg der Brieven, Boutesteyn, Leyden 1688 (a second issue of Dobell's no. 10, not a second edition), with a list of Leeuwenhoek's letters 53–60 and their contents.

Title-page   Tweede vervolg. A. Voorstad, Delft. 1689, pp. 1–350.
Letters 61–67 (May 25th, 1688–April 1st, 1689).

Letter 65 (September 7th, 1688) den Waaragtigen Omloop des Bloeds, pp. 1–30, 1688. This has a separate title-page and is numbered separately (Dobell no. 11). This accounts for the error in page numbering after p. 260 (Dobell no. 12).

Title-page Derde Vervolg. H. van Kroonevelt, Delft, 1694.
Letters 68–83 (November 27th, 1691–September 16th, 1692), pp. 351–531.

Title-page   Vierde Vervolg. H. van Kroonevelt, Delft, 1694 (Dobell no. 14).
Letters 78–83 (October 15th, 1693–April 30th, 1694), pp. 533–730.

Bound up with Register, Corn. Boutesteyn, Leyden 1695. Alphabetical index p. 34. Anonymous, Part 1, Alphabetical index on the first 10 'Tractaten' (letters 28–52, Dobell nos. 1–9). The second part was an index of the 4 'Vervolgen' (=continuations).

Volume 3

Title-plate   H. van Crooneveld, Delft. 1696.

Title-page   H. van Krooneveld, Delft, 1696, Vijfde vervolg. (Dobell no. 15).

Letters 84–96 (September 14th, 1694–November 9th, 1695), pp. 1–172.

Register (Alphabetical index).

Title-page H. van Krooneveld, Delft, 1696. Sesde vervolg. (Dobell no. 16).

Letters 97–107 (December 28th, 1695–September 27th, 1696), pp. 173–342.

Bladwyser (Alphabetical index).

Title-page H. van Kroonevelt, Delft, 1702, Sevende vervolg. (Dobell no. 17).

Letters 108–146 (April 5th, 1697–April 20th, 1702), pp. 1–452.

Bladwyser (Alphabetical index).

Volume 4

Title-plate with portrait-insert, Adrian Beman, Delft, 1718.

Title-page A. Beman, Delft, 1718 (Send-brieven).

Letters I–XLVI (November 8th, 1712–October 22nd, 1717), pp. 1–460.

Register (Dobell no. 19).

Latin Editions

The first edition of Arcana Naturae Detecta (Delphis H. a Krooneveld Title-plate 1695, H. Crooneveld) contains (Dobell no. 25) letters 32, 33, 37, 39, 40, 41, 61–92. My copy agrees with this description.

The letters 43, 42, 38, 28, 29, 30, 31, 34, 35, 36, 46, 47, 44, 45, 48, 49, 50, 51, 52 (in that order) were published for the first time by Boutesteyn Lugd. Bat. 1685–1687, in 'Anatomia Seu Interiora Rerum etc.' (Dobell no. 22).

The letters 53–60 were published by Boutesteyn, Lugd. Bat. 1687 as 'Continuatio Epistolarum' (Dobell no. 24).

The letters 93–107 appear for the first time in Latin as 'Continuatio Arcanorum,' Delphis, Kroonevelt, 1697 (Dobell no. 26).

The letters 108–146 appeared as 'Epistolae ad Societatem Regiam etc.' Langerak, Lugd. Bat. 1719 (Dobell no. 27).

The 'sendbrieven' appeared in Latin as 'Epistolae Physiologicae' (I–XLVI), Delphis, Beman 1719.

The 'Opera Omnia' or 'Arcana Naturae' (Langerak, Lugd. Bat. 1722) are made up of various editions and issues; most copies are imperfect. My own copy is as follows:

Volume 1

Title-plate and title-page   Opera Omnia seu Arcana Naturae (Langerak 1722).
Indices rerum: as in Vol. II, but instead of 53–60: 61–92.
Letters 32, 33, 37, 39, 40, 41, 61–92, pp. 515. (Dobell no. 25c.) Index rerum alphab.

Volume 2

Title-plate and title-page   Langerak 1722.
Letters 43, 42, 38; Index Argumentorum Epistola 93–107 (pp. 1–192) Index rerum (Dobell no. 23a).
Continuatio Epistolarum. Title-page, Du Vivie, Haak and Langerak, 1715, Lugd. Bat. Index rerum (mentioned in letters 43, 42, 38, 28, 29, 30, 31, 34, 35, 36, 46, 47 44, 45, 48, 49, 50, 51, 52, 53–60, in this order). Letters 53–60 (pp. 124) (Dobell no. 24b). Continuatio Arcanorum Naturae Detectorum. Title-page. Langerak, Lugd. Bat. 1722. Letters 28, 29, 30, 31, 34, 35, 36, 46, 47, 44, 45, 48, 49, 50, 51, 52, pp. 258. Index triplex pp. 1–64, 1–128, 1–124 (Dobell no. 23a).

Volume 3

Epistolae ad Societatem etc., Langerak, Lugd. Bat. 1719.
Portrait. Title-page, Index rerum.
Letters 108–146 (Dobell no. 27), pp. 429. Index (alphabetical).

Volume 4

Epistolae Physiologicae. Delphis Beman, 1719 with title-plate and portrait inset (Dobell no. 28). Index materiarum. Letters I–XLVI. pp. 446. Index (alphabetical).

LITERATURE

General works

COLE, F. J. (1937) Leeuwenhoek's Zoological Researches, Annals of Science, **1**, 1, 2.

o

COLE, F. J. (1938) Microscopic science in Holland in the 17th Century, J. Queckett Microscopical Club, Ser IV, **1**, 2.

DOBELL, C. (1932) Antoni van Leeuwenhoek and his little animals, London–Amsterdam. 2nd ed. New York 1958.

HAAXMAN, P. J. (1875) Antony van Leeuwenhoek, de Ontdekker der Infusorien, Leiden.

HARTING, P. (1876) Gedenkboek van het 200-jarig Herinneringsfeest, 's Gravenhage en Rotterdam.

SCHIERBEEK, A. (1950, 1951) Antoni van Leeuwenhoek, Leven en Werken, 2 vol. Lochem, pp. 526, 78 figs.

SINGER, C. (1950) A History of Biology, New York.

VANDEVELDE, A. J. J. (1922–26) Leeuwenhoekiana, (10) Kon. Vlaamsche Academie voor Taal en Letterkunde.

Many notes in 'The Collected Letters of A. van Leeuwenhoek' (1939–). Amsterdam, Zwets and Zeitlinger.

Chapter 2

CATALOGUS (1747) van het vermaarde kabinet . . . van wijlen A. van Leeuwenhoek.

CITTERT, P. H. VAN (1934) Descriptive Catalogue of the Collection of Microscopes in the Utrecht University Museum, Groningen.

CLAY, R. S., AND COURT, T. H. (1932) The History of the Microscope.

DISNAY, A. N., HILL, C. F., AND WATSON-BAKER, W. E. (1928) Origin and Development of the Microscope (Catalogues of the Royal Microscopical Society).

KINGMA BOLTJES, T. Y. (1941) Some Experiments with Blown Glasses. Antonie van Leeuwenhoek, **7**, 61.

STAR, P. VAN DER (1953) Descriptive catalogue of the simple microscopes, Rijksmuseum voor Geschiedenis der Natuurwetenschappen, Leiden.

VANDEVELDE, A. J. J. (1927–29) Bijdragen tot de Bibliographische Geschiedenis van het Microscoop. Verslagen Kon. Vlaamse Academie.

Chapter 3

CHAPMAN, A., CHASTON, (1931) The Yeast cell: what did Leeuwenhoek see? J. Inst. Brewing, XXXVII.

COHEN, B. (1937) On Leeuwenhoek's method of seeing Bacteria, J. Bact., 4.

COHEN, B. (1937) The Leeuwenhoek Letter (9th October, 1676), Baltimore.

COLE, F. J. (1926) The History of Protozoology, London.

DOBELL (1932) See general works.

KLUYVER, A. J. (1952) Leeuwenhoek Lecture: The Changing appraisal of the Microbe, Proc. Roy. Soc. B. **141**, 147.

Chapter 4

COLE, F. J. (1930) Early Theories of Sexual Generation, Oxford.

MEYER, A. W. (1938) The Discovery and the Earliest Representations of the Spermatozoa, Bull. Inst. Hist. Med., VI, 89.

MEYER, A. W. (1939) The Rise of Embryology, Stanford University Press.

SCHIERBEEK, A. (1952) Het probleem der Bevruchting in de loop der tijden, Meded. Kon. Vlaamse Acad. v. Wetenschappen enz. XIV, no. 12. Brussel.

Chapter 5

COLE (1937) See general works.

OYE, E. L. VAN (1952) A. van Leeuwenhoek en het Bloed., Med. Kon. Vlaamse Acad. v. Wetenschappen, XIV, no. 10.

Many notes by Dutch scientists in 'The Collected Letters.'

Chapter 6

BODENHEIMER, F. S. (1928) Materialien zur Geschichte der Entomologie bis Linné. Berlin, 2 vols.

COLE (1937) See general works.

BÖHNER, K., AND OEFELE, F. V. (1933) Geschichte der Cecidologie, Mittelwald, Bayern.

OUDEMANS, A. C. (1926–37) Critical Survey of Acarology, 9 vols., Gravenhage.

SCHIERBEEK, A. (1947) Jan Swammerdam, Lochem (a monograph) pp. 280, 28 plates; idem. Notes on the History of Cecidology in 'The Collected Letters,' Vol. VI.

Chapter 7

COLE (1937) See general works.

DOBELL (1932) See general works.

BAKER, J. R. (1952) Abraham Trembley, 1710–1784. London.

Chapter 8

HALL, H. C. VAN (1834) Verhandeling over A. van Leeuwenhoek, en zijne verdiensten voor de Plantkunde. T. v. Natuurk.,
Geschiedenis en Physiologie. I. Amsterdam.

Many notes by G. van Iterson, H. H. Janssonius, W. K. H.
Karstens, Miss A. Kleinhoonte and J. Schoute in 'The Collected Letters,' Vols. 3, 5.

Chapter 9

HOOYKAAS, R. (1950) De Oudste Kristallografie. Chemisch
Weekblad. **46**, 438.

WIELEN, P. V. D. (1932) Ant. v. Leeuwenhoek. Pharmaceu-
tisch Weekblad. 1239–1257.

In 'The Collected Letters,' Vol. 3, E. J. Dijksterhuis on Leeuwenhoek's mathematics; Vol. 6, A. Schierbeck, Leeuwenhoek
as Wine-gauger.

Chapter 10

BAAS BECKING, L. M. G. (1924) A. van Leeuwenhoek, Immortal Dilettant. Sci. Monthly, New York, XVIII, 547.

MEYER, A. W. (1937) Leeuwenhoek as experimental biologist.
Osiris, **III**, 103.

STIMSON, D. (1949) Scientists and Amateurs, A History of the
Royal Society. London, New York.

WOLFF, A. (1950) A History of Science, Technology, and Philosophy in the 16th and 17th Centuries. London, 2nd ed.

¹ Leeuwenhoek's name has been spelt in a number of different ways. On his birth certificate he is called Thomas Philipszn (i.e. son of Philip), without a family name. He at first signed himself Antonj Leeuwenhoeck, but after 1685 he usually wrote Antonj van Leeuwenhoek. The final j was an alternative way of writing i. The Christian name should be pronounced with the stress on the second syllable.

² After the invention of the microscope—about 1610—there followed until about 1660 a period of orientation in microscopy. Malpighi (1661), Hooke (1665), Swammerdam (1669), Grew (1671) form, together with Leeuwenhoek (1673), the fraternity of the 'classical' microscopists.

³ Thus Newton complained, as late as 1684, that it was impossible to hold a 'philosophical meeting' at Cambridge, '. . . for want of persons willing to try experiments.'

⁴ This certificate is shown on the portrait painted by Verkolje.

⁵ This date is given in the old style of calendar reckoning. The English text of this quotation is taken from Dobell.

[*See next pages for notes 6 and 7.*]

⁸ This letter 18 (dated October 9th, 1676) was first published in the *Philosophical Transactions*, XII, p. 821, 1677, but it was not included in the old Dutch editions (nor in the Latin) of Leeuwenhoek's works. Dobell has given an excellent new translation of the Dutch manuscript in his book 'Leeuwenhoek and his little animals' (1932), and Barnett Cohen has edited a photographic reproduction with a very good English translation in 'The Leeuwenhoek Letter' (1937). An English translation and the Dutch text, annotated by Prof. Dr. A. J. Kluyver, appeared in 'The Collected Letters,' p. 60.

[6] 'A table of the Focal Distances of Mr Leeuwenhoek's microscopes, Calculated, by an inch scale divided into 100 parts; with a computation of their magnifying powers, to an Eye that sees small Objects at 8 inches, which is the common Standard' (Baker, 1740).

Microscopes with the same focus	Distance of the focus	Power of magnifying the diameter of an object	Power of magnifying the Superficies
	Parts of an inch	Times	Times
I	$\frac{1}{20} = \frac{5}{100}$	160	25,600
I	$\frac{6}{100}$	133 nearly	17,689
I	$\frac{7}{100}$	114 nearly	12,996
3	$\frac{8}{100}$	100	10,000
3	$\frac{9}{100}$	89 almost	7,921 almost
8	$\frac{1}{10}$	80	6,400
2	$\frac{11}{100}$	72 something more	5,184 something more
3	$\frac{12}{100}$	66 nearly	4,356 nearly
2	$\frac{14}{100}$	57	3,249
I	$\frac{15}{100}$	53 nearly	2,809 nearly
I	$\frac{1}{5}$	40	1,600

26

[7] Miss Rooseboom has given the following data:

	M8a	M8aa	Hxm	Aalkijker					Utr.	Antw.
				I	II	III	IV	V		
Shape of the lens	Bi-convex	—	Bi-convex	Plano-convex	Plano-convex	Plano-convex	Plano-convex	Bi-convex	Bi-convex	Bi-convex
Diameter of diaphragm (object side) mm.	0·7	1·4	0·9	1·8	1·9	1·2	—	1·1	0·5	
Diameter of diaphragm (eye side) mm.	0·6	1·2	0·9	1·2	1·5	1·0	1·0	0·4	0·8	
Magnification	100	—	90	32	50	50	65	150	270	100
Diameter of field of view (mm.)	65	—	135	60	70	65	50	45	70	
Numerical aperture	0·13	—	0·12	0·08	0·13	0·08	0·12	0·15	0·4	
Resolving power (in μ)	4·0	—	4·0	6·0	5·0	5·0	4·0	3·1	1·4	1·09
Thickness of lens in mm.	1·8	—	1·05	1·25	1·6	1·6	2·0	1·8	1·1	2·5
Focal length in mm.	2·5	—	2·8	8·0	5·0	5·0	3·8	1·7	1·0	
Radius of curvature of the lens, in mm.	2·5	—	2·5	4·0	2·5	2·5	1·9	1·7	0·75	
Condition of lens	Good	Missing	Good	Good	Good	Good	Good	Damaged	Damaged	Good

Printed in Great Britain by Purnell and Sons Ltd, Paulton, Somerset
for Abelard-Schuman Ltd, 38 Russell Square, London WC 1
and 404 Fourth Avenue, New York 16, NY

DATE DUE

NOV 18			
NOV 10	DISCARD		
NOV 24			
OCT 18			
DEC 4			
DEC 18			
JUN 21			